QUANTUM MECHANICS AND OBJECTIVITY

QUANTUM MECHANICS AND OBJECTIVITY

A STUDY OF THE PHYSICAL PHILOSOPHY OF
WERNER HEISENBERG

by

PATRICK A. HEELAN, S.J.,

M.A. (N.U.I.), PH.D. (ST. LOUIS), PH.D. (LOUVAIN)

MARTINUS NIJHOFF / THE HAGUE / 1965

66-7718

PRINTED IN THE NETHERLANDS

TABLE OF CONTENTS

PART II REALITY IN QUANTUM MECHANICS
The Ontological Structure of Atomic Systems

PART III THE STRUCTURE OF PHYSICAL SCIENCE

CHAPTER TEN: LOGIC AND LANGUAGE OF SCIENCE

PREFACE

Quantum mechanics has raised in an acute form three problems which go to the heart of man's relationship with nature through experimental science: (1) the public objectivity of science, that is, its value as a universal science for all investigators; (2) the empirical objectivity of scientific objects, that is, man's ability to construct a precise or causal spatio-temporal model of microscopic systems; and finally (3), the formal objectivity of science, that is, its value as an expression of what nature is independently of its being an object of human knowledge. These are three aspects of what is generally called the "crisis of objectivity" or the "crisis of realism" in modern physics.

This crisis is studied in the light of Werner Heisenberg's work. Heisenberg was one of the architects of quantum mechanics, and we have chosen his writings as the principal source-material for this study. Among physicists of the microscopic domain, no one except perhaps Bohr has expressed himself so abundantly and so profoundly on the philosophy of science as Heisenberg. His writings, both technical and non-technical, show an awareness of the mysterious element in scientific knowledge, far from the facile positivism of Bohr and others of his contemporaries. The mystery of human knowledge and human subjectivity is for him an abiding source of wonder. Heisenberg is far from the naive realism of the great scientists of the past, yet too much of an empirical investigator to espouse the deductionism of Spinoza and Leibniz which exerted such a pull, for example, on the elder Einstein. It is not surprising then that he situates himself uneasily within the perspective of critical philosophy, but of critical philosophy in crisis. For this reason, the modern European continental philosopher feels closer to him in spirit than does, perhaps, his Anglo-American counterpart.

The epistemology of quantum mechanics has up to now been studied almost exclusively through the works of Bohr and many studies and doctoral theses exist in English of Bohr's philosophy. Heisenberg's philosophy has been curiously untouched. I surmise for a number of reasons. In the first place, he has always declared his attachment to the Copenhagen School and implied that he shared Bohr's philosophy of science. In fact, as this study shows, his philosophical outlook, except for a short period when he collaborated closely with Bohr, was very different and became increasingly so with the passage of time. In the second place, he is the most metaphysical of modern scientists and the genre of philosophical writing on physics in recent years has been dominated by a British and American school which tends to place metaphysics somewhere between mysticism and crossword puzzles.

The method employed exclusively in this work, and outlined in chapter one, is that of an analysis of "horizons", that is, of the kind of cognitive intentionality-structure implicit in the conduct of a systematic investigation. The kind of investigation we are interested in is, of course, a scientific investigation. An intentionality-structure is composed of a noetic and a noematic aspect which are correlative to one another. The noetic aspect is an open field of connected scientific questions addressed to empirical experience; the noematic aspect is the response obtained by scientific experiment from experience. The totality of actual and possible answers constitutes a horizon of actual and possible objects of human knowledge and this we call a *World*. The World is the source of meaning of the word "real". "Real" is then defined as what makes its appearance directly or indirectly as one of the objects in the World. But as objects can be of many kinds, the sense of "real" also is ambiguous. We find it necessary to distinguish different classes of objects: public and private objects, intelligible and sensible objects, empirical, phenomenal and bodily objects, objects of mere thought or supposition and, finally, objects in the strict (or formal) sense which are affirmed as *beings* or *noumena*.

We found it necessary to distinguish *reality* from the *criterion* of reality for us, and *real* from *being*. The two traditional extremes of empiricism and rationalism can then be defined with respect to the horizon of objects conceived to constitute the World of real things. Empiricism identifies the *real* with *being* and both with objects of empirical intuition, that in, with bodies. The meaning of real and the criterion of reality are identified. Rationalism identifies *being* with *intelligible object*, and tends to employ the term "real" for the object of empirical intuition, which, however, is regarded as alien to being. With this schema, it is possible to trace the movement of Heisenberg's thought, that is, the changing meaning he gave to such key words as *reality*, *being* and *objectivity*, during the critical period of the development of quantum mechanics and the subsequent modification of his position as he grew older.

Our point of departure is the horizon of classical physics into which Heisenberg entered as a young student and which is the epitome of extreme rationalism.

Chapter two is an account of the historical origin of the quantum theory in its two forms; the quantum mechanics of Werner Heisenberg and the wave mechanics of Erwin Schrödinger. Heisenberg's discovery of quantum mechanics was accompanied by a dramatic insight into the structure of physical science: a quantity which could not be observed in principle (a non-observable quantity) should not be part of a physical theory. This discovery brought about the first major change in the intentionality-structure of physics since the time of Galileo. Heisenberg's master-insight implied a conversion from the rationalist intentionality characteristic of classical physics to a predominantly empiricist one. A major influence in the explicit formulation of this change of outlook was Bohr whose *principle of complementarity* was eventually (and reluctantly at first) accepted by Heisenberg.

In chapter three, we analyse the philosophy of complementarity as sketched first of all in Bohr's works and then in the early writings of Heisenberg. We find that it includes a theory of scientific method, and a philosophical outlook on *reality*, *objectivity* and *causality*.

In chapters four and five, we are concerned with an exposition and critique of the complementarity account of scientific method. In the first place, complementarity states that our concepts of physical properties have basically the same logical structure as those of everyday life. This thesis, depends upon a theory of knowledge called *psycho-physical parallelism*. We show that there are two logically different sets of concepts in every physical theory; a set founded upon relations *to us* (*operational* and *observational concepts*) and a set founded upon relations *to things* (*explanatory concepts*). Because of this, psycho-physical parallelism is not a satisfactory account of scientific knowing. Moreover, the place of *observable symbols* (pointer readings, etc.) and their counterpart in *mathematical symbols* is not sufficiently accounted for in the complementarity view of scientific method.

The second problem in scientific method concerns the function of the measurement process in physics. Heisenberg implies that, since it is part of the activity whereby we contact and so observe physical reality, it has a disturbing effect on reality and tends to limit our access to the objective properties of atomic realities (*This is the perturbation theory of measurement*). In keeping with the distinctions we have made between properties-for-us and properties-for-things, we assert that the measuring process is essential to the definition of a physical property as a property-for-things. Hence the so-called perturbation is an essential element in its definition; it is not extrinsic to the objective property nor has it anything to do with a limitation of our access to physical reality.

The third problem (chapter five) in scientific method concerns the *public objectivity* of quantum mechanics. Heisenberg asserts the inescapable presence of a "subjective element" in the quantum theory. By this he means two things: (i) the failure of the (Kantian) category of "substance" for an atomic system (from which it follows that an atomic system cannot be given a "realistic" description of universal validity, i.e., for all observers), and (ii) that the act of observation – as a *private conscious act* – resulting in the "reduction of the wave packet" effects the suppression of physical correlations (or superposition states) and so changes a physical aspect of reality.

With respect to (i), we answer by distinguishing between the *observable symbol* (which may or may not constitute a coherent causally related phenomenal object) and the *thing or property symbolised* (whose consistency is to be judged by the non-contradictory character of the mathematical theory, and whose reality is manifested through an observable symbol). With respect to (ii), we defend the view that the formation of a *mixture* from a *pure case* is a logical operation determined by the antecedent choice of the kind of experimental data to be observed and that any physical changes effected are consequences of the activity whereby the measuring instruments are set up and the results obtained.

The intervention of the scientist-observer's subjectivity then is no different in quantum physics than in classical physics. The nature of the quantum physical object, however, is different; for, while in classical physics this is an *idealised normative* (and hence *abstract*) object, in quantum physics the object is an *individual instance of an idealised norm*. In classical physics, differences of individual instances from the ideal norm are treated by a statistical "theory of errors"; in quantum physics the "errors" of conjugate properties are found to be concretely linked and for this reason the statistical part of a quantum mechanical explanation cannot be separated from its non-statistical part. An atomic system, then, is represented in the quantum theory by a *virtual ensemble* in which both the physical variables (as properties-for-things) and their distributions about their means (or expectation values) are linked within one unitary formalism. The *Indeterminacy Relations* are expressions of the *concrete character* of the object of quantum mechanics and of the interrelated character of the "errors" of conjugate quantities.

During the course of our attempt to separate the physiognomy of the *strict object* from the matrix of scientific methodology in which it makes its appearance, we demonstrate the thesis that *no* physical thing or property in so far as this is an explanatory element in physics – whether it be in classical or in quantum physics – is *per se* representable in sensibility (i.e., *per se* observable). It becomes *per accidens* observable only through the occurrence of appropriate *observable symbols* associated unambiguously with the physical object in question.

In chapter six, we discuss various opinions on the essence of the *Correspondence Principle* which relates classical and quantum physics in *limiting cases*. We point out that the ambiguity in the various views is due to the multiplicity of possible limiting processes by which a classical theory can be obtained from a quantum theory; for besides the vanishing of the quantum of action limiting procedures can also be applied to the rules of correspondence (or interpretation) which link the mathematical formalism to experimental observations. For example, if the quantum rules are retained, then a classical statistical particle theory is obtained: if, however, the quantum rules are changed so as to make the operators correspond to numerical averages of quantities taken over a small interval of time at a given epoch, then classical particle mechanics is obtained. On the basis of these considerations we vindicate the *completeness principle* for the quantum theory.

Part II, comprising chapters seven, eight and nine, is concerned with the ontological structure of atomic systems. Chapter seven examines various notions current among physicists on the meaning of *reality* and its *criterion for us*. These are divided for convenience into two classes: one of predominantly *rationalistic* tendency of which Einstein (Senior) is chosen as a classic example, and another of predominantly *empiricist* tendency, illustrated by some aspects of Wigner's thought.

In chapter eight, we consider Heisenberg's ontology at length. From an early and predominantly empiricist phase, he passed to a predominantly rationalist viewpoint on nature; not, however, back to the rationalism of Cartesian mechanism, but to one inspired almost totally

by the transcendental philosophy of Kant. We find that he is also
strongly influenced by Plato, while his more recent adoption of
Aristotelian terminology (of the terms *dunamis* or *potentia*, and *universal* or *primary substance* or *matter*) does not really indicate a significant change in his outlook. It provided him, however, with a solution
to the problem of what noumenal reality to associate with a quantum
mechanical system like an elementary particle. The noumenal reality
associated with a quantum mechanical system is, he says, a *dunamis*
(or *potentia* or *objective tendency*) related to the act of observation. The
act of observation completes its actuality by actualising one of the
possibilities (or eigenstates) represented by its state vector. Heisenberg
also identifies *energy* with Aristotelian *primary matter*. Heisenberg's
Practical Realism, as he calls his philosophy, remains however a
Kantian type idealism.

In chapter nine, we present our solution to the problem of the
objective realism of a scientific theory. First of all, the notion of *reality*
is examined in the light of the polymorphism of human cognitive
activity. This enables us to overcome the fundamental and unharmonised duality (part empiricist and part rationalist) in Heisenberg's
thought. We show that the structure of human cognitive activity is
realistic. We next examine the relationship of a part (e.g., the nucleus)
to the whole (e.g., of an atom) in a compound microscopic system. We
find that the part is not an *actual part*, but can be called a *virtual part*.
We examine also the function of energy in physics as a universal
invariant. We find that energy has not the properties of an Aristotelian
prime matter, but is a condition of possibility characteristic of a
particular physical milieu and that it governs the kinds of systems and
processes permitted by the milieu.

In Part III (or chapter ten), we gather together synthetically the
clues suggested by the preceding analysis on the logical structure of a
physical theory. We find that physics as a science depends upon the
articulation of two Worlds: a World-for-us (described by *operational* or
observational concepts) and a World-for-things (described by *explanatory
concepts*). The duality of World explains the use by the physicist of two
languages: an *observation language* and an *explanatory language*.

ACKNOWLEDGMENTS

The author wishes to thank Monsignor Louis de Raeymaeker, President of the *Institut Supérieur de Philosophie*, and vice-rector of the Catholic University of Louvain, together with the professional staff of the *Institut*, for the instruction, guidance and inspiration to which the author owes so much. The author wishes also to express his indebtedness to Fordham University, New York, and to Princeton University, New Jersey, where, as a Visiting Fulbright Fellow, he prepared the scientific part of this work. In the collegiate chapel on the campus of Princeton there is a transcept window dedicated to the benign patrons of learning. Among these, fittingly, with Augustine the philosopher-theologian and Bacon the scientist, Cardinal Mercier, founder of the *Institut Supérieur de Philosophie* is immortalised.

The author owes a warm personal tribute of respect, admiration and gratitude to Professor Jean Ladrière of the Catholic University of Louvain, who in 1959 encouraged him to undertake this work and then, while generously making available to him his own great learning, left him nevertheless entirely free to pursue the insights out of which this book eventually came. This work was presented as a doctorate thesis to the Catholic University of Louvain in 1964.

The author also wishes to thank the Very Reverend Charles O'Conor, S.J., Provincial, for making time and resources available for this research; Professor Eugene Wigner of Princeton University for many valuable conversations on the epistemology of quantum mechanics; M. H. Heelan, Esq., for the infinite patience with which he reviewed the style and expression of the manuscript; and Mrs Irene Sheils for typing the manuscript so expertly thereby relieving the author of so many pains.

Fordham University, 1965

PART I

OBJECTIVITY IN QUANTUM MECHANICS

THE EPISTEMOLOGICAL STRUCTURE OF
QUANTUM MECHANICS

CHAPTER ONE

INTRODUCTION

SECTION I: METHODOLOGICAL INTRODUCTION

Intentionality and World

The *intentionality structure* of an act of knowledge is the orientation of a human knowing (*noetic*) subject towards a horizon of knowledge constituted by a certain ordered context of objects given or to be given in experience. The empirical answer to a particular noetic orientation on the part of a human subject constitutes a *noema*.

The total ordered context of all actual or possible objects is called a *World*. It is the "horizon of all horizons" [1]. Kant took the notion of World to be a regulative idea or principle [2]. We do not accept this view. Nor do we accept the view that the World is a derivative notion secondary to the objects it contains and a mere totalization of these objects. The World is prior to its elements; it gives reality to its elements. The World may be considered rather as the broad field of human activity which as far as the active and inquiring person is concerned is presupposed by the activity of doing and questioning. It is part explored and part mystery. But the part which is mystery is not totally hidden. It is foreshadowed in outline as the full domain which human empirical activity can attain.

The noetic intention is an attitude of inquiry, of questioning attention to what is given in experience, accompanied by an active search for what is already foreshadowed in some way by the question even before any reply is obtained from the World. A noetic intention then constitutes a reality-outline to be filled, and the filling of that

---

[1] A. de Waelhens, *La philosophie et les expériences naturelles* (The Hague, Nijhoff, 1961), p. 110.

[2] I. Kant, *Critique of Pure Reason*, trans. by Norman Kemp Smith, (London, Macmillan, 1963), p. 392.

outline does not occur all at once, but is a progressive process in which
there are always more questions at any stage than there are answers.
Hence, while noetic intentions are invariant elements in the structuring
of the World, the World is not a static ensemble of noemata given once
and for all, but it is an organically growing system which evolves and
develops according to the special intentionality-laws which rule it. The
intentionality structure of a particular question then prefigures the kind
of answer it will receive; not, however, that the question determines
that there should be an answer, but that an answer, if one should be
given, will appear not as totally disconnected with reality but as a
looked-for reality within an already ordered context which we called a
World, which is the horizon of the horizons of all empirically answer-
able questions. As M. Dondeyne says: "Consciousness is essentially
intentional; . . . it presents the form of a dialectical relation between
a 'noesis' and a 'noema', the two calling to each other, and constituting
one another in an indissoluble unity . . . If an intention is to be
actualised, it must be incarnated in a behaviour *sui generis* called
'observation' . . . ; for example, if a countryside seems to be dark and
sad, it is in part because I am sad discouraged; but it is also equally
true that sunless weather contributes to my sadness" [1].

A *noema* is an object of concrete factual knowledge. It is affirmed by
a knowing subject as "real" – not in isolation from the rest of reality –
but precisely because it partakes in the reality of a total ordered context
of actual and possible realities which is his World. True reality, then,
for a subject is his World. It constitutes the horizon in which single
isolated events have a place if and only if they are real.

It follows from this that there are many Worlds. Each epoch of
human history and each epoch of one's own personal history has its
World. Childhood, youth, maturity and old age have their Worlds,
different perhaps for different people. There is the World of the
physician, the World of the sportsman, the World of the husband, the
World of the wife. We shall be concerned with the World of the physical
scientist in the twentieth century.

Each of these Worlds represents some subject's sphere of reality; but
to see it as such, and to explore the richness of the reality revealed in
its perspective and illuminated by its light, one must be placed at the
noetic pole of such a World. The failure to do so leaves the World an

[1] A. Dondeyne, *Foi chrétienne et pensée contemporaine*, (Louvain, Publications Universit.,
1961), pp. 25–26.

incoherent jumble of pseudo-facts, distortions, and "abstractions" [1]. How often have we not heard humanists and philosophers mock at the scientific culture of our day, while remaining profoundly ignorant, not only of its depth, complexity and articulation, but also of the human motivations of the scientists themselves. On the other hand, scientists have on the whole little sympathy with a humanism which often speaks pityingly of the agony of the human condition but with such self-pity that no energy is left to better it. C. P. Snow has described with a tough of bitterness this polarisation of our culture between two hostile Worlds: "The great edifice of modern physics goes up", he wrote, "and the majority of the cleverest people in the modern world have about as much insight into it, as their neolithic ancestors would have had" [2]. If, then, it is our aim to explore the reality structure of modern physics, a necessary condition of this is that we learn to place ourselves sympathetically at the noetic pole of perspective of a working scientist. To fill this position, we have chosen one of the creators of modern physics who, because of this, is also one of its most authentic interpreters, namely, Werner Heisenberg. He will be our guide to the World of quantum physics and the interpreter to us of its reality.

A World is, at least in some way, *given in and through experience.* Husserl defined it to be the "totality of objects that can be known through experience, known in terms of orderly theoretical thought on the basis of direct present experience" [3]. The objects in question were for Husserl "given primordially in perception". It is our intention to enlarge the notion of World to include the horizon of objects known through the interpretation of data. Though not given "primordially in perception" these interpretative objects, like atoms, electrons, etc., are none the less given through experience, and constitute an extension of the notion real. They comprise a total ordered context of objects, whose "reality" is based upon the interpretation of sensible signs which reveal to the inquiring mind of the scientist the presence of these objects in an experimental situation. The structure of this new World of hidden objects revealed through sensible signs will be investigated in the course of this dissertation.

---

[1] "The properties of a physical theory are formulated in abstract mathematical language. Let us compare them with a musical score. For those who cannot read notes, the musical score is dead, but the man who understands them hears the melody in them". C. F. von Weizsäcker, *The World View of Physics* (London, Routledge and Kegan Paul, 1962), p. 35.

[2] C. P. Snow, *The Two Cultures and a Second Look* (Cambridge, 1964), p. 15.

[3] E. Husserl, *Ideas* (London: 1931), pp. 51–2. Cf. also A. de Waelhens, *op. cit.*, pp. 107–121, *Le Monde*.

A World is also intersubjective. It is a public arena in which many people meet. People meet by orienting themselves mutually to one another in a common World or in the ground common to their Worlds. This overlapping of Worlds is a condition *sine qua non* of communication between people. The range over which they can communicate, and the extent to which they can be in contact, is determined by how much of a common World they share. A World, then, is essentially a meeting place of a group – of young or old, of philosophers or scientists. It is a condition of cooperative science. Moreover, since the inquiring mind of man is never still but ceaselessly tries to unveil more and more the potential riches of reality, the World itself is also affected by the scientific enterprise.

Objects and Objectivity

If the true home of real objects is a World, and if a World is constituted by publicly accessible objects, how are these to be described? Is there one kind of public object or are there many kinds? Does the kind of object affect the meaning of "reality"?

In the first place, there are two kinds of *public objectivity:* one is the public objectivity of the *idea* (or *concept*), and the other is the public objectivity of a *reality*. The former is the property of whatever has an exact and precise definition independently of particular places, times and factual judgements. It belongs, not to any World, but to the realm of ideas. The latter, however, makes its appearance in a World of real things, as the object of factual judgements, founded upon concrete empirical experience; and hence its description contains an irreducible element of the imprecise and indeterminate. Whatever can be precisely and determinately defined by us is not as such a reality but an idea.

In the second place, let us describe three classes of objects, and give names to the *in-itself* correlate of each, viz., the correlate of each which transcends consciousness.

The first is an object which is a unity, identity, whole and the stable subject of properties, and which may be either an object given in perception (viz., a phenomenal object) or a constructed object – like an electron – which is linked by us to existence through sensible signs. The transcendent being correlated with this object is called by us a *thing* [1]. This first class contains the following class as a sub-division.

The second class is that of phenomenal objects. This is the class of objects "given primordially in perception". It might be described as a

---

[1] We are using "transcendent" in the Kantian sense of "noumenal" or "in-itself".

stable subject of perceptible properties in a spatially organised World. In so far as this is represented in consciousness, we shall call it a phenomenal object; in so far as it transcends consciousness we call it a *body in the strict sense*. Allied to the notion of body as the transcendent correlate of a phenomenal – and therefore perceptible – object, there are two limiting concepts which we shall include under the name *body*. They are: (1) what is conceived to have determinate spatial coordinates at each instant – as, for example, a classical particle – even though it is not perceptible (provided it is capable of yielding some sign of its presence); and (2) a *field* as an infinitely extended medium for three-dimensional wave motions (provided also that it is capable of yielding a sensible sign of its presence).

The kind of objectivity which is found here is one based upon the *exteriority of subject and object in perception, and we call it empirical objectivity*. This may be subdivided into *phenomenal objectivity* (for a phenomenal object) and *bodily objectivity* (for a body). This kind of object, however, is not so constituted by the act of knowing that it is entirely separated from or independent of all subjectivity; for exteriority implies its correlate, viz., the interiority of a subject, from which it cannot be divorced. It is, then, always an object-for-me.

Is it possible for a knowing subject to know itself objectively? It is evident that a contradiction would arise if we were to state that within the relation of objectivity just described, the subject could become object. However, there is a kind of objectivity in which even the subject as such can participate; that is an objectivity in which the object is constituted as simply independent of a relation to a subject: this we call *formal objectivity*. It belongs to whatever is affirmed as a virtually unconditioned object on the basis of evidence. In physics, the evidence is provided by a process of experimental verification. This kind of object we call an *object in the strict or formal sense*, or simply a *strict object;* for its *intention* is simply to express *what is*, independently of the act whereby I know it as an object-for-me. The transcendent correlate of an object in the strict of formal sense is, evidently, an *individual existing being*, or a *law of being*.

Subjectivity

We define *subjectivity* to be the absence of the corresponding kind of objectivity. *Subjectivity* then is a word with many meanings which are differentiated by the different types of objectivity defined and distinguished above.

Reality and its Criterion

Let us distinguish, moreover, the *meaning* of "reality" from the *criterion* of reality. The first defines what is meant by the term; the latter is that on account of which a thing is said by a certain knower to be real: in our case, it is a sign through which its reality is manifested to us.

It is clear that the word "reality" will have as many meanings as there are different kinds of objects which can be conceived to constitute a World. For example, if a World is conceived in the naively realist sense to be an organisation of bodies in the strict sense, then "reality" will mean "whatever can be perceived as a body". It is the characteristic empiricist understanding of the term, where meaning and criterion are scarcely separated. If, taking a more sophisticated view, the objects constituting the World are expressed by the limiting concepts of classical particle and classical field, then "reality" will mean "whatever has determinate spatial coordinates at every instant, or whatever is an infinitely extended medium for three-dimensional wave motions"; sensibility merely providing the presentative sign of their presence. Interpreting the latter condition as merely a criterion of reality, then the first part of the definition gives the characteristic rationalist meaning of the term presupposed by classical physics.

Our own view is that an ontological World is constituted only by an ordered context of *objects in the formal sense,* that is, of such objects as are affirmed as virtually unconditioned objects – i.e., as *beings* – on the ground of evidence provided by a critical scientific process of testing and verification.

We hold, moreover, that the criterion of physical reality for us is extrinsic to its meaning, since we have no intellectual intuition of physical reality. Our view then of physical reality can be summarised in the two following points: (1) "reality" means "an object taken in the strict or formal sense within the ordered context or horizon of such objects which constitutes a World"; and (2) the criterion of reality for us is a manifestation of its presence in the World through sensible signs. This last is a rational criterion and not a purely sensible one, since the recognition of the significance of the sensible sign is a rational and not a purely sensitive act.

The World of Modern Physics

Among the many different Worlds, each defining reality for some subject, one interests us in particular, viz., the World of twentieth-century physics. How is one to investigate the reality structure of the World of modern physics? M. Dondeyne, I think, has given us the clue. Stressing the correlation between *"noesis"* and *"noema"* in science, he writes: "If the scientific object is to reveal itself to human consciousness with the structure which belongs to it, it must be approached with a scientific attitude; it must be *questioned* scientifically; that is, one must go out to meet it with hypotheses and verify these hypotheses *in* the object; that is why science – even empirical or positive science – is not the result of a purely passive attitude towards the world, but it is 'something to be done' in the strict sense of the term" [1].

If science is something the scientist does, then the method of investigating the reality structure of modern physics is not to look *out there* at things in the naively realist sense of the *natürliche Einstellung* of Husserl in the hope of seeing electrons, protons, etc., but to reflect on the noetic intention of the scientist, to see what kind of objects he was looking for, and by criticising this to arrive at a correct notion of the ontological content of physics. The scientist has unveiled by his experimental activity new but shadowy physical objects. Do they belong to the scientist's World of reality in the same way as do the tools and instruments of his research? Does scientific methodology imply a certain meaning of "real"? Is it necessary that scientists have a common meaning for "reality"? The pre-philosophic (or natural) outlook of a physical scientist in post-classical physics is rarely that of naive realism. Electrons, protons, etc., make their appearance in the context of a World-out-there of bodies but they are never directly given as bodies in this World. A cursory survey of current scientific writings shows that two kinds of natural pre-philosophic outlooks prevail among scientists to-day. There is the empiricist-positivist outlook on the one hand which is content with practical results, with what works. There is the rationalist outlook on the other hand which assumes on the basis of the Newtonian tradition that only that which has well defined space-time coordinates is a reality. Only a careful analysis of scientific method and a criticism of the pre-philosophic conceptions of modern scientists will succeed in separating the true noema which is the object in the formal sense of physics from the intentionality-structure of the scientific method through which it is revealed.

An investigation of this sort of the intentionality structure of quantum mechanics is of interest not merely to philosophers but also

---

[1] Dondeyne, *loc. cit.*, p. 26.

to many physicists; for many to-day are deeply disquieted by the conceptual paradoxes which lie at the foundations of quantum physics. This has led to a revival of interest in many of the old controversies and to some new ideas, but largely to a resurrection of old ones which had been forgotten. Professor Wigner sums up the situation thus: "The orthodox view [viz., of Bohr, Heisenberg and the Copenhagen School] is very specific in its epistemological implications. This makes it desirable to scrutinise the orthodox view carefully and to look for loopholes which would make it possible to avoid the conclusions to which the orthodox view leads. A large group of physicists finds it difficult to accept these conclusions and, even though this does not apply to the present author, he admits that the far-reaching nature of the epistemological conclusions makes one uneasy". Professor Wigner then adds the following suggestion: "The misgivings, which are surely shared by many others who adhere to the orthodox view, stem from a suspicion that one cannot arrive at valid epistemological conclusions without a careful analysis of the *process of the acquisition of knowledge*" [1]. The chapters that follow are largely a commentary on this remark.

SECTION II: PHILOSOPHICAL INTRODUCTION

Introduction

The period of crisis in physics which led to the construction of the quantum theory was viewed at the time by those intimately connected with it, not merely as a change in physics, but as a change in philosophic perspective about man, reality and human knowledge. Bohr, impressed by the difference between our everyday vision of a solid material world and the description given of it in quantum mechanics, came to the conclusion that a physicist can no longer take an uncritical attitude towards truth, reality and human knowing. All our expressions as he wrote, "bear the stamp of our customary forms of perception from the point of view of which the existence of the quantum of action is an irrationality... In consequence of this state of affairs, even words like 'to be' and 'to know' lose their unambiguous meaning" [2]. Acknowledging the importance of clarifying at the start our basic philosophical vocabulary, it is nevertheless with great reluctance that

---

[1] E. P. Wigner, "The Problem of Measurement", Address to the American Physical meeting at Washington, D.C., 1962; published in *Amer. Jour. Phys.*, XXXI (1963), p. 6.

[2] Niels Bohr, *Atomic Physics and the Description of Nature*, (Cambridge: 1961), p. 19.

we propose to preface our discussion of the intentionality of quantum mechanics with what might be called a set of implicit definitions of terms. We do it with reluctance because such an attempt risks becoming a pedantic monologue, in which a series of profound problems are taken up in rapid succession and reduced to capsule formulae; for if a set of definitions is to be a useful tool – and this is the purpose of our introduction – it must incorporate in some way a definite viewpoint, implying a certain problematic and a certain tentative solution. Our excuse, then, is that such a sketch is necessary; and we wish to prefix it with an apology for seeming to treat *omnia scibilia* in a few pages.

Being and Truth

Being is what the content of any object taken in its strict or formal sense expresses or tends to express, though whether *truly or falsely* will depend on the presence or absence of certain criteria. *Truth* is the relation of conformity between the strict object of a judgement and the being represented by it. We understand this relation to mean no more and no less than what is found in the critical analysis of well-made judgements. We assume, of course, that we know from experience when we have made a well-made judgement. From an analysis of well-made judgements, we derive the conclusion that a true theory is one which is asserted to be independent of all subjectivity (i.e. independent of its being an object of knowledge) and posited in the absoluteness of being. This we have called formal objectivity, and it is constituted by an act of the mind which affirms that a sufficient set of conditions is fulfilled to provide a rational ground for the affirmation of absoluteness (or unconditionality).

The strictly real or ontologically real is the kind of being affirmed or affirmable of bodies or things, and it is expressed by the content of the strict object of true judgements in physics and in everyday life. Restricting ourselves to the subject matter of physics, we can say that, since we lack intellectual intuition of these, they are presented to us in knowledge as *conditioned* by the necessity of manifesting their reality through some criterion. An object of knowledge, then, which does not itself contain the criterion of its reality, may remain a mere thought-object to be considered or supposed (whether as a pure idea or as a phenomenal object). If, however, the criterion of reality is given simultaneously with it, the object of knowledge may be asserted as strictly or ontologically real.

The criterion for the reality of an individual factual object is that it should be given – either directly or indirectly – in perception, and recognized rationally as such. The criterion for the truth of a physical theory is contained in the elaborate process of scientific testing and verification; and it is fulfilled only asymptotically with an ever increasing probability. However, a distinction has to be made between the *criterion* and the *truth* of a theory. The criterion is generally a complex and unending set of tests, predictions and experiments which comprise an open set of conditions linked asymptotically with the truth of the theory. However, the set of conditions is not a linear chain of conditioned conditions regressing indefinitely, but a set of true factual judgements which individually and collectively provide the evidence for the physical theory. It is part of the physicist's training to know how to construct a set of strategic questions whose affirmative answer would constitute a sufficient basis to justify the affirmation of the theory as a virtually unconditioned object. By this we mean that the theory is *conditioned* by certain criteria (viz., the evidence) but that it is also *virtually unconditioned* because sufficient strategic criteria – judged by experienced scientists to be such – are present to justify this assertion. By the formula a *true physical theory*, we intend no more than what has been just described.

Three kinds of cognitive activities which have their place in the complete act of human knowing are of special interest for the work that follows: first of all, acts of perception or sensible intuition; secondly, acts of conceptual understanding; and thirdly, acts of affirmation or assertion. The object expressed by an act of the first kind is a body taken in the strict sense; the object expressed by an act of understanding is the content of a pure idea or concept; the object expressed and constituted by an act of affirmation is an object in the strict or formal sense. In the case of a factual judgement, this last act falls on a content which is defined by a concept and whose reality is indicated in perception.

Without going deeply into the genesis of these three kinds of acts and their articulation within one complex act of knowing, we propose to mention certain factors concerning them which are of great importance for the study we are about to make, and which are, in a sense, the philosophical frame of reference of the author [1].

---

[1] The elements of the philosophical analysis which follows have been strongly influenced by Bernard Lonergen's work, *Insight, A Study of Human Understanding* (London: Longmans, 1957), and the set of articles entitled "The Concept of the *Verbum* in the Writings of St. Thomas Aquinas" written by him and published in *Theological Studies*, VII (1946), 349–392; VIII (1947), 35–79, 404–444; X (1949), 3–40, 359–393.

Concepts and Abstraction

The first is the nature of *conceptual knowledge* and of the act called *abstraction* in which a concept is produced [1]. A concept is an act of knowledge answering the question: What is so and so? which, as Lonergan says, is really a subtle way of asking: Of what are such and such sensible data a manifestation? It expresses a nature, which is not, however, an individual incommunicable nature, but a nature in so far as this specifies and can be shared by an ensemble of individuals. It seems to be, then, on the one hand, the highest common factor of a set, and for this reason it is said to *abstract* from all that is not common to members of the set; as, for example, from particular places and times: on the other hand, however, it is also the *production* or *construction* of an *ideal norm* with respect to which individuals can henceforth be compared as to the degree in which they conform to its rule or depart from it; as, for example, when a circle is defined as the locus of points equidistant from a fixed point called its centre. This last example also brings out an essential aspect of the ideal norm – it always expresses a *relation* between terms which are themselves mutually and implicitly defined by the relations; for example, in the case of the circle, the relation is one of distance equality between the centre and any point on its circumference.

Thus there exist two classes of theories regarding the mental operation of abstraction. We call the first the *impoverishment theory of abstraction* [2]. It assumes that we know individual cases first in their particularity and then, by a kind of comparison akin to factorial analysis, we isolate the highest common factor of the lot, and from this we form an impoverished representation valid for a class of things. This assumes that the content of the concept was actually known prior to abstraction though not as the common factor of a class of individual instances, and that abstraction is a conscious act of comparing mental contents. Against this theory, we object that no matter how many instances have been considered, others remain unconsidered and among these there may be some which would induce a modification of the content of the concept if they were known. The impoverishment theory of abstraction serves the useful purpose of helping to make *empirical generalisations* which are,

---

[1] As we are not concerned with the different moments in the abstractive process, we are taking *abstraction* globally to signify the whole process.

[2] We have taken the name from a remark made by E. Cassirer: "As long as we believe that all determinateness consists in constant 'marks' in things and their attributes, every process of logical generalisation must indeed appear an impoverishment of the conceptual content'". *Substance and Function* (New York: Dover, 1953), p. 22.

however, only preparatory organisations of data, and a way of schematising experience in order to present this to the inquiring mind under the form of *regularities to be explained*. The explanation is achieved by the second form of abstraction.

The second theory is the *enrichment theory of abstraction*, and this starts from contrary premises. It asserts that knowledge of particular cases with which we start *does not* contain the concept, but that this is the end-product of a complicated set of steps in which the analysis of sensible data is of key importance. The preliminary steps are the formulations of hypotheses, their testing and their acceptance or rejection according to their value as *abstract or ideal norms* from which the sensible data do not systematically diverge. During this process certain data supposed to be irrelevant are left out; as, for example, particular places and times, the exclusion, however, is not made on the basis of a factorial analysis, but as a consequence of the kind of hypothesis which is projected. The *abstract norm* is expressed as a *manifold way of being related to other things or to a knowing subject*. The ideal norm then does not suppress the particular cases or exclude them from consideration in order to isolate a common "note", but it retains them implicitly as *sample terms in a relational structure* which constitutes a *systematic totality* [1]. This process then results in the positive enrichment of the knowledge of particulars, (a) by the formulation of sets of relations between them, and (b) by the definition of an ideal norm or law, viz., a mathematical equation or function, from which the sensible particulars do not systematically diverge. We might call this moment that of the formation of the *pre-philosophic scientific concept*. The final moment is the formation or constitution of the object in the strict or formal sense. This occurs when one takes cognizance of and reflects on the fact that the phenomenon so analysed is only a *symbol of a transcendent being* [2]. In this symbol the *ideal relational norm* corresponds to a formal similarity of essence; the *unsystematic departure* from the norm corresponds to an essential openness to multiplicity; and the *systematic totality* in its fulness and concreteness corresponds to the notion of World as an ordered context of noemata.

The former theory of abstraction, viz., the *impoverishment theory* of abstraction, has a long history, and traces of it are to be found in

---

[1] Ernst Cassirer calls the systematic totality so related an *Inbegriff*, *ibid.*, p. 22.
[2] Cf., B. Lonergan, *Theological Studies*, x (1949), 3–40, especially p. 9.

Aristotle [1] and in most of the medieval philosophers, including Aquinas [2]. It is, however, especially characteristic of the philosophy of Scotus [3], and of the strong tradition which, through Ockham and the late medieval Nominalists, reached the modern era in two streams; the empiricism of Hobbes, Locke and Berkeley, and the rationalism of Descartes and Leibniz.

It is based upon the conception of the human mind as a mirror in which is formed a passive reflection of what is out there in the external world [4]. Its notion of objectivity is limited to the kind that is founded upon the relation of *exteriority*, and which we have called *bodily objectivity*. Its view of concept-formation can be described as a process of generalisation in which concepts are analysed, compared and factorised. This exclusive view of concept-formation is – in one way or another as we shall show later – characteristic of scientists and philosophers of science of nearly every school with, however, some notable exceptions; as, for example, Einstein, Hermann Weyl and others. One important consequence of this theory is that, among scientists of the classical rationalist tradition, reality in the concrete is taken to be as specific and detailed as the content of the defining concept; that is, if a scientific theory defines its concepts numerically – as, for example, mass, position, etc. – then individual physical systems are taken to have in reality, and independently of observation, precise and determinate values of these up to an infinity of decimal places. This is a view of the meaning of "reality" which we find among philosophers of a rationalist background and of physicists of the classical school. Its insufficiency lies in its failure to advert to the fact that numbers apply to sensible data which are merely *symbols for us* of the concrete reality which they manifest.

The *enrichment theory of abstraction*, of which there are suggestions in Aristotle and Aquinas, has its advocates in modern times in the philosophies, for example, of Ernst Cassirer and Hermann Weyl [5]. We

---

[1] Ernst Cassirer claims to find in Aristotle a classic exposition of this theory of abstraction (*Substance and Function*, pp. 4–9). However, such an opinion is not sufficiently nuanced. Aristotle, after all, was the first to introduce a special faculty of the intellect to account for the *production* of the intelligible form. It was through the development of this clue that the enrichment theory of abstraction obtained its characteristic feature, viz., of being *constructive* of intelligibility. Cf. also, *ibid.*, pp. 18–26.

[2] As, for example, in the *Summa Theologica*, I, p. 85, a.1.

[3] Cf., B. Lonergan, *Theological Studies*, VII (1946), p. 372.

[4] For Scotus, sensibility was only the *occasion* of the formation of the mental image; for Aristotle, sensibility was *instrumental* in its formation.

[5] Ernst Cassirer, *Substance and Function, loc.cit.;* Hermann Weyl, *Philosophy of Mathematics and the Natural Sciences* (Princeton: 1949).

differ from the last two in seeing *two* moments in the process of object-formation. The two moments are: (a) that in which the sensible data are synthesised and the first (scientific or pre-philosophic) enrichment occurs and (b) that in which the second and final (or ontological) enrichment occurs and the strict object of knowledge is formally constituted.

Human knowledge in the course of its development uses (a) as a moment to reach (b); but finding (a) difficult and laborious – as e.g., in scientific research – while its completion and fulfilment in (b) is accomplished naturally and easily, the existence of two moments in the full act of knowledge can easily be overlooked. Moreover, as the difficulty of scientific research lies in (a), it would be possible for us to agree with scientists and philosophers of science in their account of (a) without thereby accepting fully their views of knowledge and reality. Thus Ernst Cassirer and Hermann Weyl share the view that the enrichment of sensible data occurring at the stage of the synthesis of sensible data consists in the formation of an *ideal relational norm from which individual data do not systematically diverge* [1]. However, their view of the meaning and criterion of reality and of the relation between sensibility and intellect is different from ours. In the enrichment theory of abstraction, *the pre-philosophic scientific concept* is not an *apodictic norm* as a Scotist norm must logically be, but merely a *possible norm* which is verified *in the data up to a certain degree of accuracy in fact.* Since it is an ideal norm, individual cases are expected to diverge from it, but not in a way that can be defined. Moreover, individual cases are known to be random samples of the ideal norm. And finally, it expresses something absolute only in so far as this is a subject or a term of a set of relations within a systematic totality; this implies the ontological position that we know no physical thing in its absolute nature except in so far as this is a part of a World.

Deterministic (Causal) Theories [2]

The preceding analysis reveals the possibility of two kinds of physical theories: deterministic or causal theories and probabilistic theories.

---

[1] Cassirer, *loc. cit.*, and Weyl, *loc. cit.* We differ from both these authors in stressing that the ideal relational norm is derived *from* sense data and expresses the intelligibility present in these data, without being itself a sense datum. In our view, the sense data, when understood, is understood to be a symbol whose inner function and purpose is to manifest being; i.e., not merely the phenomenal being of the symbol, but the transcendent being to which it points. The metaphysical position of both Cassirer and Weyl is that of Neo-Kantian Idealism.

[2] In keeping with common usage among physicists, *deterministic* is here taken as synonymous with *causal*.

The first kind is represented by the construction of an ideal relational norm for sensible data from which individual cases do not systematically diverge [1]. Consider, for example, Newtonian Mechanics. A particle is defined as the subject of six independant phase-space variables, viz., position and momentum in each of three directions; all six are relative to a frame of reference and to a unit. The laws of mechanics define by implicit definition how these are related through their time derivatives and through force (also relative concepts) with one another [2]. All variables are described operationally through appropriate measuring processes which map them onto the number field [3]. The equations are such that, given the initial values of all phase-space variables and the form of the law of force, the state of an isolated system at any future (or past) time epoch can be calculated exactly. This kind of theory is called a *deterministic or causal theory* [4], since it allows the calculation of the future or past state of an isolated system if its state is given at an arbitrary origin of time. The isolated system in question, however, is not a real system, for all its variables – even position – are supposed to be defined with an infinite degree of precision, while data on any real system are obtainable only up to a certain degree of accuracy [5]. Hence the system described by Newton's Laws is one which is represented (or symbolized) by an idealised conceptual model; in other words it is an *ideal or abstract norm*.

A deterministic theory serves two functions: (1) it connotes a self-defining set of physical relations, and (2) it yields a set of mathematical functions, parametrised by the time, which describe how a set of ideal measure numbers changes with the time parameter. It does not directly describe an individual physical system but it compares this with a constructed norm, viz., with a set of precise mathematical functions of which it is to be regarded as a random sample of one.

---

[1] This process may also be called *idealisation;* it is the product of enriching abstraction.

[2] This is sometimes called a *constitutive definition*. For the nature of *implicit definition,* cf., D. Hilbert, *Grundlagen der Geometrie* (Leipzig: 1930); Weyl, *loc. cit.*, chap. I; and *infra,* chap. IV.

[3] The relation between the implicit (explanatory) definition and the operational description is discussed below in chap. IV.

[4] A *deterministic* of *causal physical system* sometimes denotes simply a classical particle or a classical field, for it is supposed that such a system is always governed by deterministic laws, even when the behaviour of the system at every instant is not fully known, as, e.g., in a classical thermodynamical ensemble.

[5] Cf. M. Born, "The statistical interpretation of quantum mechanics", *Science*, CXXII (1955), 675–679; M. Born and D. J. Hooton, *Proc. Camb. Phil. Soc.*, v (1956), 52, 281. Born and Hooton show of what little significance in fact is the knowledge of precise initial conditions even for a classical system.

Probabilistic Theories [1]

A *random case* is one which is selected from a *range* of possibilities and belongs to a random set. A random set is a collective with the following properties: (1) it is a finite sample of elements, which are individual, concrete and independent instances of the *same ideal norm*; (2) and such that there exists a unique function which expresses the *ideal relative frequency of occurrence* of each of the possibilities. By *ideal* in the second context we mean that the relative frequencies of any finite sample of sufficiently large size is not *significantly different* from the ideal relative frequency. This property is also called the *ergodic hypothesis*.

This definition has the advantage that it incorporates the essential features of von Mises's classic definition without being open to the attacks arising from the infinite collectives in his explanation and the type of limiting processes he envisaged [2]. First of all, since only the relative frequencies are counted in any set, the order in which the elements arise or are considered is immaterial to the calculation. This satisfies von Mises's condition of *irregularity*. Secondly, his limiting frequencies in an infinite collective are no more than ideal relative frequencies in the sense we have just defined and can be understood and postulated independently of the limiting procedure which he described. They do not then belong to any concrete finite or infinite collective, but to an ideally constructed norm for all random sets of a given type. Finally, von Mises's condition of *convergence* satisfies our definition and is perhaps the most reasonable translation of it into mathematical language – i.e., if it should be proved to be consistent with itself.

The present author's intention is not to propose a new basis for the calculus of probabilities but rather to bring out one essential epistemological aspect of the classic concept of probability, namely, that the classic concept is itself an ideal abstract norm and not a concrete value belonging to any actualisable collective. Hence, as von Mises himself was aware, the postulation and subsequent testing of statistical hypotheses involves the same set of epistemological problems as the construction and testing of deterministic hypotheses [3].

---

[1] The exposition of the following paragraphs owes much to chap. IV of *Insight* by B. Lonergan, and to *Probability and Induction* (Oxford: 1949), by W. Kneale.

[2] R. von Mises, *Probability, Statistics and Truth* (New York: 1939). Cf., W. Kneale, *Probability and Induction*, pp. 150–167.

[3] "The relation of the theory of infinite collectivities and observation is... essentially the same as in all other physical sciences", R. von Mises, *loc. cit.*, p. 125, quoted by W. Kneale, *loc. cit.*, p. 160.

Our definition, however, adds a new element of importance for it states what constitutes a member of a random set. It is whatever is judged to be a concrete and independent instance of the same ideal norm among a set of such independent instances. The ideal norm connotes the choice of a type of theory and of a set of initial conditions. The similarity of initial conditions is to be judged according to the *practical criteria of significance* employed by experienced physicists. Similar instances of the same ideal norm are not the same as equiprobable instances, since there is no reason why the distribution of instances in a random set need be governed by a constant probability measure. Random instances do not, however, differ significantly and systematically. Individual concrete cases which are similar instances of the same ideal norm of this sort constitute a *random set*.

Our definition, moreover, has the added advantage of explaining how random sets occur in experience and how they are related to our way of knowing. They occur as sets of individual instances which in experience exhibit *a margin of "uncertainty"* or *"error"*. This uncertainty is the same as the deviations from the mean which Laplace took to be the subject matter of probability. We ascribe them to a different cause [1]. The results of a set of experiments, judged by practical criteria to be performed under similar conditions, are generally distributed on a range of values and the relative frequencies of occurrence of the different values in the set tend in general to a limit. This limiting frequency is a new ideal norm, however it is conceived. In the classic definition it is conceived to be the limiting relative frequency within an infinite series of individual instances. In any event, whether it be defined in this way or as we suggest, it describes not the actual results of any test but a new abstract concept which is called by the physicist the *probability of occurrence* [2].

According to the view which we have expressed, probability laws arise out of the very nature of scientific knowing and are an essential complement of deterministic (or causal) theories. They depend on the latter for the definition of the variables, of the initial conditions and of the law of development or evolution of the physical system. They

---

[1] As R. L. Ellis writes: "Mere ignorance is no ground for any inference whatsoever: *ex nihilo nihil*", *Mathematical and Other Writings*, ed. G. Walton (Cambridge: 1863), quoted by W. Kneale, *loc. cit.*, p. 151.

[2] A *probability* or a *probability measure* is generally predicated of a particular value or of a particular interval in the range respectively; the distribution of frequencies in an ensemble based upon a set of probabilities is called a *statistical distribution*. An individual case considered as a sample of *one* taken from a statistical distribution is often called a *virtual ensemble*.

complement deterministic laws because they succeed in organising material which a deterministic law omits as irrelevant to its type of synthesis, namely, the distribution of variations of concrete measured data from the ideal mathematical law [1].

We shall have occasion later on to return in more detail to the points outlined above for the epistemological analysis of probability is one of the central problems for the interpretation of quantum mechanics [2].

Probability and Human Ignorance

Our epistemological position can be clarified by comparing it with the common – and classic – view that probability laws in physics are based upon human ignorance of aspects of the concrete situation due to such factors as, for example, the complexity of the situation or to the crudeness of measuring instruments. This was the view of Bernoulli, Laplace and Leibniz, and its classical exposition is found in Laplace's work, *A Philosophical Essay on Probabilities* [3]. It is the view most commonly held by physicists and philosophers of science to-day.

Let us distinguish two types of ignorance. The first type belongs to the man who sees a series of near-similar events happening but does not know enough about them individually to be able to deduce the law in the series. The second belongs to the man who knows that there is *no determinate law* in the series, viz., that the series is merely factual and nothing more. We hold that probability laws are founded upon the latter state of mind and that it is not really a kind of ignorance but a kind of negative knowledge. Because of this negative judgement, he can limit the possibly significant material of any series to relative frequencies of occurrence within the series, that is to *probabilities*.

It can be objected that if, like Laplace's demon, we had exact knowledge of the initial conditions of a physical process, we should then be able to predict the behaviour of the system and the need for merely probabilistic laws would vanish. This objection is based upon an ontology and an epistemology different from that defended by the present author. One source of this objection is the rationalist *Principle of Sufficient Reason* as, for example, understood by Laplace and Leibniz, which is intimately connected with the rationalist view of reality. Another source of this objection is a view of knowledge very

---

[1] Cf., Lonergan, *Insight*, chap. IV, pp. 46–51.

[2] *Infra*, chap. II, section VII, pp. 38–41.

[3] Pierre Simon, Marquis de Laplace, *A Philosophical Essay on Probabilities* (New York: 1951), chap. II; and also W. Kneale, *loc. cit.*, pp. 1–21.

like the Scotist one, according to which individual cases are thought to be known in individual concepts from which common notes are abstracted by conceptual analysis. If this were so, then each system would have to have the same infinite precision as their factorised norm.

On the contrary, we hold that our initial knowledge of particular cases is defective and potential. This is eventually enriched by abstraction with the construction of an ideal, abstract or limiting case which has the property that particular cases do not diverge systematically from it or that particular cases can tend to it but never reach it. The non-systematic element which enters into our knowledge of individual cases will be discussed more fully below and is connected with the essential function of sensibility in the acquisition of knowledge and in the formulation (or constitution) of the strict object in which alone physical reality is truly known by us [1].

It may be conceded to the objection that since we have no intellectual intuition of physical reality, there is always more in any particular case than we can ever know. However, this lack of knowledge is not simply a question of decimal places. The particularity of a physical reality does not consist in the supposed possession of an infinity of exact decimal places. It would be mistaken to assume that we approach asymptotically the individuality of a particular case by accumulating more and more of these. There is a limit, as every physicist knows, to the significance of any decimal series. The reason for this is that decimal places and number-mapping in general belong to the human manipulation of the sensible symbols through which reality is known by us. They are instruments useful to an abstractive mind like man's, but not to a non-abstractive intelligence which would know the concrete case in its particularity and within the context of a concrete pattern of relations. Not having sensibility, the non-abstractive intelligence would have no need to map these relations on a number field as we are accustomed to do.

For this reason we think it misleading to say that probability laws arise out of human ignorance. In one sense probabilities indicate an absence of comprehensive knowledge, viz., the intellectual intuition of concrete physical reality. In a more important sense, however, they are founded not upon ignorance but upon the abstractive character of human scientific knowing and represent an irreducible factor of scientific knowing. The contrary view which we oppose is connected

[1] *Infra*, chap. ii, pp. 30–32 and chap. v, pp. 107–9.

moreover with an ontology and epistemology which we find impossible to justify [1].

Probability of Evidence

There is another sense of *probability* which should be carefully distinguished from the former sense: it has been variously called "acceptability", "credibility", "reasonableness" etc. [2]. It is not a concept but a quality or mode of the affirmation of the judgement. It is the estimate of the connection between the *evidence* for a judgement or a theory made on the basis of the process of a scientific verification, and the *necessary ground* that the judgement or theory could be rationally affirmed in a virtually unconditioned judgement. A virtually unconditioned judgement – which is a *certain judgement* – is one for which sufficient conditions for a reasonable affirmation are known to be fulfilled in fact. If, however, the inquiry has not been pursued to a definitive conclusion, then a *probable judgement* can be made on the basis of insufficient evidence, where the probability in question is not measured in terms of ideal frequencies but in terms of how far or how near it is to the status of being *virtually unconditioned*. Judgements about probabilities in the first sense (viz., as ideal frequencies) can be *either* certain judgements *or*, if the evidence is not complete, merely probable judgements, where *certain* and *probable* here refer to the particular sense of probability discussed in this paragraph.

Summary

The method, aim and presuppositions of the present work are outlined in this chapter. The subject matter of the book is the quantum mechanics of Heisenberg. Its aim is to state and analyse the problematic called the "crisis of objectivity" or the "crisis of reality" in quantum physics. Its method is an analysis of the intentionality structure of quantum physics as Heisenberg conceived it to be and, through a critique of this, to arrive at a clarification of the problem and of its presuppositions, and eventually at a tentative solution. Section I deals with the method and aim of the dissertation; Section II defines some of the philosophical vocabulary used in the text.

[1] Cf. O. Costa de Beauregard, *Le second principe de la science du temps* (Paris, Seuil, 1963), pp. 47–49.

[2] "Acceptability" is used by W. Kneale, *loc. cit.*; "reasonableness" is used by R. Braithwaite in *Scientific Explanation* (Cambridge: 1953); B. Russell uses "credibility" in *Human Knowledge. Its Scope and Limits* (London: 1948); Karl Popper uses "verisimilitude" in *Logic of Scientific Discovery* (London: 1959); R. Carnap's "degree of confirmation" serves the same purpose.

CHAPTER TWO

THE DISCOVERY OF QUANTUM MECHANICS

SECTION I: WERNER HEISENBERG AND QUANTUM MECHANICS[1]

Introduction

The insight which led Heisenberg in 1925 to the formulation of quantum mechanics was in some respects as momentous as the Copernican insight into the ordering of the heavenly bodies; for it changed the point of perspective from which physicists since the time of Copernicus were accustomed to look at the world. It changed a viewpoint about the world which had become *classical* and tumbled down a pile of certainties on which the physics of three hundred years had been based. Heisenberg called these the "ontology of materialism", that is, the certainty that nature was out there, solid and material, infinitely accessible to objective description, in which the goal of each succeeding generation of scientists was the conquering of yet another decimal place [2]. Quantum mechanics showed that this goal was a mirage; it revealed the presence of a subtle subjectivity at the very heart of the scientific enterprise, and, by so robbing the mind of its solid support, left it as Heisenberg said, "suspended as over an unfathomable abyss" – the unfathomable and mysterious abyss of its own subjectivity [3]. Even in the moment of its conception, Heisenberg, Bohr and the small circle of intimates who surrounded them, knew that the structure of quantum mechanics was of critical importance for more than scientific method. They realized that it destroyed one ontology of nature and profoundly affected the science of the intimate structure of the human mind.

---

[1] We intend to use the terms "quantum mechanics" or "matrix mechanics" for Heisenberg's theory of 1925; "wave mechanics" for Schrödinger's theory of 1926, and "quantum theory" as a term of general meaning applicable to both.

[2] W. Heisenberg, *The Physicist's Conception of Nature*, (London: 1958) p. 14.

[3] W. Heisenberg, *Philosophic Problems of Nuclear Science*, (London: 1952), p. 117.

Quantum mechanics

It is our intention to use Werner Heisenberg as our guide to the philosophical world of quantum physics, since he was both one of its founders and one of its most profound interpreters. He was one of the many who, in the decade of 1920–1930, were busy with the problem of trying to reconcile quantum phenomena with the traditional physics of Newton, Maxwell and Laplace. Traditional physics was a very proud and impressive scientific structure. It was endowed at that time with an authority derived chiefly from its logical splendour, which made it a norm not merely for all science, but for all rational thinking. Traditional physics was not just a particular view of physics which might itself be subject to revision. It was *classical physics*. It was, therefore, with an experience like that of a conversion, that physicists found themselves turning inward to examine critically the revered foundations of what they and their colleagues had believed in for three hundred years.

Many of the original founders of the quantum theory have told us about the transition that was then taking place in physics. Some accounts date from the early days of hectic and almost evangelical enthusiasm; others were written in retrospect and in a calmer mood. But all conveyed the conviction that as a result of the discoveries of that decade man had reached a new level of consciousness about the world, himself and the horizon of human knowing [1].

The first successful synthesis of quantum with classical physics was made by Heisenberg in the summer of 1925 [2]. His ideas were taken up immediately by Born, Jordan and Dirac who helped to bring them to

---

[1] The principal accounts of the events of this period recounted by Bohr and Heisenberg are: N. Bohr, "Die Entstehung der Quantenmechanik", in *Werner Heisenberg und die Physik unserer Zeit* (Braunschweig: 1961), IX–XII; and "Discussion with Einstein on Epistemological Problems in Atomic Physics", in *Albert Einstein: Philosopher-Scientist* (New York: Library of Living Philosophers, 1949), 199–242; W. Heisenberg, "Quantenmechanik" Nobel Prize address, in *Les Prix Nobel en 1933* (Stockholm: 1935); "Fünfzig Jahre Quantentheorie", *Naturwissen.*, XXXVIII (1951), 49–55; "Erinnerungen an die Zeit der Entwicklung der Quantenmechanik" in *Theoretical Physics in the Twentieth Century*, a Memorial Volume to Wolfgang Pauli, ed. by M. Fierz and V. F. Weisskopf (New York: Interscience, 1960).

[2] Werner Carl Heisenberg was born in Würzburg on the 5th of December, 1901. He studied physics at Munich under Sommerfeld, Wien, Pringsheim and Rosenthal, entering the university in 1920. During the winter term of 1922–23, he studied under Born, Frank and Hilbert in Göttingen. He obtained his Ph. D. at Munich in 1923, and his *venia legendi* (*Habilitation*) at Göttingen in the following year. In the winter of 1924–25, he was Rockefeller Scholar under Bohr at Copenhagen. In 1926 he was appointed lecturer in theoretical physics at the University of Copenhagen. In 1927 he became Prof. Ord. of theoretical Physics at the University of Leipzig. He was awarded the Nobel Prize in 1933. He became Director of the Kaiser Wilhelm Institute, Berlin in 1941, and Prof. Ord. at the University of Berlin. In 1946 he helped to found the Max Planck Institute for Physics in Göttingen. He is now Director of the Max-Planck Institut für Physik und Astrophysik, Munich.

near logical completion within a year. Schrödinger, working on the ideas of de Broglie, published his celebrated theory of wave mechanics in the spring of 1926, followed soon by a proof of the equivalence of his theory with that of Heisenberg. Within a year, the permanent lines of a new physics were drawn.

The most detailed and authoritative account of the germination of the ideas which constituted quantum mechanics was written by Heisenberg himself for the memorial volume, *Theoretical Physics in the Twentieth Century*, and dedicated to the memory of Wolfgang Pauli [1]. It was written while Pauli was still alive but, by the time of its publication in 1960, Pauli was already dead. In this detailed account of the course and development of his thought in those days, full of personal reminiscences and documented by extracts from his letters of that period, Heisenberg singles out Pauli as his principal confidant and correspondent in the dialogue preceding the fruition which took place in his mind in the summer of 1925.

The questions which were in the air at that time among physicists were three: the anomalous Zeeman effect due to electron spin, the Exclusion Principle, and the foundations of what is now called, the old quantum theory. This was the quantum theory of Bohr and the wave-particle dualism of de Broglie. It was generally thought then that these three questions were connected parts of one problem. As it turned out, however, they were separate questions, each contributing in its way to the overthrow of the scientific outlook of classical physics [2].

As we are principally interested in the change in intentionality marking a shift in the noetic orientation of the physicist-Heisenberg, we shall start at the logical *terminus a quo*, namely, the intententionality-structure characteristic of the classical physics.

SECTION II:
INTENTIONALITY STRUCTURE OF CLASSICAL PHYSICS

Classical physics is characterised by a naively realist outlook (called "materialist" by Heisenberg) towards physical reality. The physical reality envisaged by the intentionality-structure of classical physics is one made up of the kind of parts which are objectifiable in Space

---

[1] W. Heisenberg, *Erinnerungen* usw., *loc. cit.*

[2] Cf., for example, Sir Edmund Whittaker, *History of the Theories of Aether and Electricity, 1900–1926* (London: Nelson, 1953).

and Time. The outlook of classical physics then implies certain philosophical doctrines about (a) objectivity, (b) causality and (c) reality.

(a) The physical object has *empirical objectivity*. It is a *Gegenstand*, situated out there, *vis-à-vis* the observer [1]. The relationship between noema and noesis is one of exteriority with respect to the knowing subject. For most classical physicists, the physical real is a body situated outside them and outside all observers as such in a determinate part of space and time. It possesses that kind of empirical objectivity we called bodily objectivity. It is made up of parts which, no matter how small they may be, can be represented in a determinate fashion in space. It is composed then of parts which are in turn composed of smaller parts until the smallest parts – if there are such – disappear below the threshold of measurement, observation or empirical intuition. However, since the parts at this stage, even though no longer capable of being given in perception, can still be thought about, they are *ideal bodies*, the content of a concept constructed as a limiting case of what is given in experience. There are two such limiting cases: a *classical particle* and a *classical field*. The former has position but no magnitude; the latter is conceived to be an infinitely extended medium like a hypostatised space with just sufficient "body" to sustain vibratory motions.

It should be noted that Kant – the great philosopher of classical physics – was unwilling to allow the scientific object more than phenomenal objectivity since he believed that the realm of the thing-in-itself was unattainable by natural science. The influence of Kant's transcendental critique was not generally felt by the majority of physicists; its effect, however, in the period of crisis which was to accompany the discovery of quantum mechanics was profound.

(b) Physical objects are linked by the kind of causality which regulates their appearances in strict and orderly sequences of antecedent-consequent. For most physicists this causality was between real bodies and could be called *bodily causality*. The follower of Kant would see in it no more than *phenomenal causality*. The complete expression of this point of view is the *physical law of causality*, which is expressed as follows: "When all determinations which describe the present state of an isolated system are known, then the future of the system can be calculated" [2].

---

[1] Cf. A. Dondeyne, *La différence ontologique chez M. Heidegger* (Louvain, Inst. Sup. de Phil.) p. 11.

[2] W. Heisenberg, "Kausalgesetz und Quantenmechanik", *Erkenntnis*, II (1931), pp. 172–182; quotation is on p. 174.

(c) The physical object has the *public objectivity of a concept*, i.e. it is one which is represented conceptually in the same way by everyone. It has, then a determinate description or definition which leaves no element to be completed by private acts of observation. Public objectivity in this sense is also in the classical world-view a criterion of physical reality: it is, accordingly, a rationalism in which the meaning of "reality" is the content of an infinitely precise conceptual definition from which is excluded whatever is represented by the vague and imprecise elements recorded by concrete empirical intuition; "reality" means "what can be precisely defined even to an infinity of decimal places". This almost Platonist notion of reality dehumanised and taken out of its context in a World of real beings is what Heidegger called *Vorhandenheit* [1]. This is itself one of the extremes in the dialectic of being in Western philosophy; it is the end of one swing of thought and the beginning of another which was to be set in motion by the discovery of the quantum theory; for the first immediate effect of the quantum theory was to reinstate the immediate object of empirical intuition in the centre of science and to focus attention on the material, individual, incommunicable and concrete object of experience as part – and, to many as the whole – of the true object of scientific knowledge.

The classical notion of what constituted a real physical thing and object of physics was founded upon a Cartesian Mind-Body Parallelism in which Mind was thought to "reflect" Matter as in a "mirror" [2]. The classical scientist, then, got to know reality by making infinitely precise this image within him. All that was obscure, indeterminate or indistinct was eliminated as coming from the subject; secondary qualities like colour, taste, etc., were excluded by this criterion. Only the primary qualities of extension and its derivatives were accepted as objective elements of reality, and these only in so far as they were idealised through the assignment of infinitely exact numerical values, which were accepted as belonging to the thing in itself and not to the representation of the thing. The fund of possible physical realities, then, was made up of whatever could be represented by *idealised imaginative models*. These were limiting cases of phenomenal objects to which corresponded the three divisions of classical realities: *classical particles, structures made up of classical particles* and *classical fields*. In summary, then, the

---

[1] Dondeyne, *op. cit.*, p. 20, where the author refers to paragraphs 19, 20 and 22 of Heidegger's *Sein und Zeit*.

[2] W. Heisenberg, "The Origins of the Mechanistic and Materialistic World-View" and "The Crisis of the Mechanistic-Materialistic Conception", *Physicist's Conception of Nature*, pp. 121–179.

classical physicist oriented himself to the construction of idealised and objectifiable phenomenal objects, i.e. concretely, to an explanation in terms of classical particles, spatially constructed models and classical fields [1]. We have called this the intentionality-structure of classical physics.

Out of this account the main theme of our study arises. This is an analysis of the various kinds of objectivity in modern quantum physics with a view to separating the scientific object from the forms imposed upon it by human knowing, and with a view to studying critically the possible link between the scientific object and reality.

SECTION III:

CRISIS OF THE CLASSICAL INTENTIONALITY-STRUCTURE

Crisis

The three problematic areas of quantum physics, viz , spin, the exclusion principle and the failure of the old quantum theory, could not be reconciled with the picture of reality given by classical physics. Spin was a mysterious new dimension. The exclusion principle forbade for no clear reason the duplication of like bodies. The old quantum theory, while satisfying the classical criteria of objectivity, nevertheless allowed the electron within the atom to violate well-established classical laws. Moreover, it was found that the old quantum theory which gave good results when applied to the hydrogon atom, failed in most other cases and notably when applied to the hydrogen molecule.

Heisenberg, recounting with scrupulous care the source of his ideas, says that in October, 1923, Pauli was the source for him of a great light on the meaning of physics: model representations, Pauli said, had in principle "only a symbolic sense", they were "classical analogues for a 'discrete' quantum theory" [2]. The remark was momentous, not because it attacked any physical result, but because it attacked the intentionality-structure which supported classical physics and which hitherto was accepted as the only reasonable dynamic structure capable of generating a valid physical theory. The consequences of this

[1] Although the classical object was conceived to be something in the three-dimensional space of our experience, it was not an object of perception in the rich emotive personal way of everyday life. It was already a very abstract construction. It was because of this that Goethe and the humanists of this century and the last have cried out against the claims of physical science to represent reality truly. Cf., Heisenberg, *Philosophic Problems* etc., pp. 60–76, and C. F. von Weizsacker, *The World View of Nature*, pp. 93–94.

[2] Heisenberg, *Erinnerungen* usw., *loc. cit.*

change in viewpoint were profound. If the phenomenal object is only a symbol of reality, then reality is what lies "behind" the symbol and may possibly be unknowable. The swing away from rationalism had begun. It opened the door to the two extremes between which philosophers of physics have since been divided: *Empiricism* or *Empiricistic Positivism* on the one hand, which denies the possibility of an ontology of nature, and *Subjectivism* on the other hand, which sought the meaning of reality in evolving noetic experience alone, apart from a transcendent reality revealed through it. Heisenberg certainly rejected the former, and Pauli with him in all probability. The philosophy to which Heisenberg eventually settled down was a Kantian-style Idealism in which a tenuous thread linked the noetic experience to an unknowable noumenal term.

A Physics of "Observables"

The great insight which brought about the discovery of quantum mechanics was that physics should concern itself only with *observable quantities*. The insight came to him in May, 1925, as he was about to leave for a vacation in Heligoland. During the month of June on Heligoland he sketched the application of his idea to the anharmonic oscillator and found that it worked. This was the subject of his first paper on quantum mechanics, submitted to the *Zeitschrift für Physik*, and was received by the editor on 29 July 1925 [1].

The content of that insight was remarkable; not merely because it inaugurated a new era in physics and a new intentionality-structure in science, but because, important as it was, its precise content eludes definition. It has an air of deceptive simplicity. At first sight, it has all the appearance of a refreshingly clear, matter of fact, down-to-earth statement which delights the practical man by cutting away the myth and mystification of an entrenched tradition. And it was in this sense that it inspired a kind of iconoclastic uprising among the young, positivistically inclined physicists whose evangelical motto became "Out with metaphysics and all unobservable quantities!". A closer inspection however shows that Heisenberg's basic insight was one of Teutonic complexity of whose meaning and implications Heisenberg himself was not fully aware. We shall try to bring out some of these implications and use them to throw light on the main problem of this thesis.

[1] W. Heisenberg, "Ueber quantentheoretische Umdeutung kinematischer und mechanischer Beziehungen", *Zeit. f. Physik*, XXXIII (1925), pp. 879–893.

Heisenberg wrote to Pauli in a letter of 24 June 1925 about his master-idea: "Grundsatz ist bei der Berechnung von irgendwelchen Grössen, wie Energie, Frequenz usw., dürfen wir nur Beziehungen zwischen prinzipiell beobachtbaren Grössen vorkommen" [1]. The basic principle, he says, is to consider only relations between observable magnitudes, that is, between magnitudes which could in theory be observed.

But what is an observable? Taking the term in an unqualified sense, an observable is whatever can manifest itself immediately in experience, like heat (as felt), colour (as seen), sound (as heard), etc. At first sight, this seems to be what Heisenberg means when he criticises intra-atomic electron orbits as "lacking intuitive foundation" [2]. However, it was not Heisenberg's wish to deny the three hundred years of physics based upon the mathematisation of qualities *as measured* in order to return to a pre-Galilean or Aristotelian physics based upon qualities *as sensed*. What stimulated Heisenberg's insight was the recognition that certain variables, like the intra-atomic electron orbits, appearing in the old quantum theory, were *not measurable*. They were, in fact, not even imaginable, for the imagination cannot picture radii of 10^{-8} cm. The electron orbits were limiting cases of the imaginable and so were concepts. But in so far as imaginative representations are used, these were merely imaginative *symbols* of something that escaped the power both of imagination and of measurement. Was it, however, the absence of a true image of them or the failure of measurement technique – for the electron lacked both – which made them unobservable? We argue that it was not the mere absence of a true image; for Heisenberg continued to speak of the "observation of electrons in an atom" [3]. Many physical properties, like magnetic field, the polarization of light, etc., produce no specifically recognisable effect directly on the senses or imagination; they have no true image. Their essence is in the way they influence other things and it is not important that they should be capable of being experienced directly. We conclude then that *observable* and *unobservable* are to be defined with reference to *measurability*.

Measurability, however, is a complex notion. It involves an interaction with a measuring instrument capable of yielding macroscopic sensible data, and a theory capable of explaining what it is that is

---

[1] Heisenberg, *Erinnerungen* usw., *loc. cit.*
[2] Heisenberg, *Zeit f. Physik*, XXXIII (1925), p. 879.
[3] W. Heisenberg, *The Physical Principles of the Quantum Theory*, (Chicago: Univ. of Chicago, 1930), p. 64; the same point is also implied in the article we are considering.

measured and why the sensible data are observable symbols of it. Heisenberg's notion of observability involves all these points implicitly. The explicit dominant factor in his mind was the necessity of giving a physical quantity an "intuitive foundation" in the measuring process.

In what sense do the sensible data give an "intuitive foundaiton" to the measured quantity? Sensible data are, as we have said, *observable symbols* of the property. However, to *observe something* is in principle different from *observing its symbol*. They are distinct actions and could conceivably exclude one another. To see the word "Dublin" is not to observe Dublin, even though the word "Dublin" is the symbol of Dublin. Is then the observable of physics merely the observable symbol, or is it a real property revealed in some non-metaphorical way through the observable symbol? One of the aims of this thesis is to study the various answers given by physicists to this question. Our answer is that the observable symbol can reveal a real property if it denotes or indicates the real presence of a variable whose intimate nature, though not *per se* representable in sensibility, is known, however, in some other way and simultaneously. We take the observable symbol to be the criterion of reality for something whose nature is known only as part of a complex relational totality expressed symbolically in linguistic or mathematical terms. The something *beyond* the symbol to which it refers may be a constructed object merely immanent to the knower, or the symbolism may go further and denote a transcendent thing or property. It will be our task to establish criteria for distinguishing these two cases [1]. We call both of them *"observation in the symbol"*, and complex though the description is, the kind of process we have described is performed continuously and with ease in daily life; for the use of language is nothing more than to "observe in the word-symbol" something beyond itself, namely, its immanent sense or its (transcendent) referent.

The other important element in Heisenberg's insight was the need he saw to return to the concrete, immediate instance of a physical property as revealed in the data of individual measurements. This involved a turning away from the rationalism of classical physics with its criterion of the clear, distinct and abstract idea, and a rediscovery of reality in the individual, factual instances revealed and mediated by the act of observation. It was on account of this strong empirical

---

[1] For example, in a language the *semantic* or *formal* meaning of a word is a term or object purely immanent to the knowing subject; but its *full* or *ontological* meaning generally refers to a reality transcending the immanent term.

element – a break with three hundred years of physical tradition – that quantum mechanics marched on to the stage accompanied by a militant philosophy of Positivism and Empiricism. However, that was by and large contrary to the inclinations of Heisenberg, who remained attached to the old criterion in philosophy and sought a rationalistic explanation on a deeper level for the indeterminacy and impreciseness of the new physical object. He found it, as we shall show, in a transcendental critique of the new scientific knowledge.

SECTION IV:

QUANTUM MECHANICS, A NEW KIND OF PHYSICAL THEORY

A Theory of Operators

We shall postpone the inquiry into Heisenberg's ontology and theory of knowledge to a later chapter. For the moment we shall consider only the immanent object symbolised on the one hand by its observable symbol and on the other by its appropriate mathematical symbol.

The object called an "observable" was represented in Heisenberg's first paper by a linear algebraic operator, which Born showed had the properties of a matrix [1]. The eigenvalues of this operator gave the set of possible values of the observable [2]. The set of observables were defined theoretically in such a way as to preserve a reasonable continuity between classical and quantum physical theories in limiting cases. This latter condition was Bohr's *Correspondence Principle* which had been used so successfully in the old quantum theory: we shall return to this later on. The principal difference between classical physical theory and quantum mechanical theory was the substitution in quantum mechanics of a linear operator for the numerical variables of classical physics.

The observable as a linear operator gave more information than the corresponding classical variable. *In the first place,* its set of eigenvalues restricted the range of possible numerical values. This range ceased in every case to be a continuous range, but admitted discrete values and discontinuous jumps. Both the continuous range

---

[1] M. Born and P. Jordan, "Zur Quantenmechanik", *Zeit. f. Physik*, XXXIV (1925), pp. 858–888.

[2] The linear operator is assumed to be *Hermitian* and *hypermaximal*; the former guarantees that the eigenvalues are real, the latter that it has a soluble eigenvalue equation. Cf., John von Neumann, *The Mathematical Foundations of Quantum Mechanics*, (Princeton: 1955), pp. 153, 169.

and the discrete values were calculable, in principle, from the theory. *Secondly*, the linear operator, as Born and others were immediately to show, gave also a probability-distribution governing the ideal frequency of occurrence of particular values of the observable within a set of independent observations [1]. And *finally*, since the coordinate observable did not commute algebraically with the corresponding momentum observable, their probability distributions – but not their ranges of possible values – were correlated. The derivation of that correlation, called the Indeterminacy (or Uncertainty) Principle, was made by Heisenberg in 1927 [2].

Novelty of Quantum Mechanics

Quantum mechanics was a new kind of physical theory. In the first place, it determined the possible range of values of its own variables, which classical theory left – except in exceptional cases – to factual observation. In the second place, it allowed the calculation not merely of the ideal norm (or expectation value) of sets of concrete data, which was the aim of classical deterministic theory, but also the manner of distribution of individual instances about the expectation value. Here was another radically new result. For, while in a classical deterministic theory like Newtonian mechanics, concrete measured data are distributed about means randomly, independently of the other variables and generally according to a Gaussian law (unless there is reason to assume a different error curve), in quantum mechanics on the other hand the distributions are random, but not independent, and their forms depend on the initial boundary conditions as well as on the equation of development (the Schrödinger equation of the system). In classical physics, statistical theories are separated from deterministic theories: the function of the latter being to define by implicit definition the elements and properties of the underlying statistical ensemble [3]. The great originality of quantum mechanics is that it both

[1] M. Born and P. Jordan, *loc. cit.* Heisenberg attributes the probability-interpretation to Born and Pauli, adding that the idea had also occurred to himself, cf., *Erinnerungen* usw. cf. also P. A. M. Dirac, "Physical Interpretation of Quantum Dynamics", *Proc. Roy. Soc.*, cxiii (1927), pp. 621–641.

[2] W. Heisenberg, "Ueber den anschaulichen Inhalt der quantentheoretischen Kinematik und Mechanik", *Zeit. f. Physik*, xliii (1927), pp. 172–198.

[3] Most statistical theories, like statistical thermodynamics, are under some aspects equivalent to deterministic theories; since the new variables (temperature, entropy, etc.) are defined implicitly with respect to a set of interrelated variables. The statistical element enters when these new variables are identified with certain limiting statistical concepts applied to an underlying ensemble. However, the deterministic part in a classical statistical theory does not go so far as to define the elements and properties of the underlying ensemble. For this purpose it has to rely on a distinct theory like Newtonian mechanics.

defines the properties of the elements of an ensemble and predicts their frequency distribution within the ensemble *in one formalism*. This involves a double interpretation of the same formulism as we shall see.

SECTION V:
QUANTUM MECHANICS AND WAVE MECHANICS, 1926

Wave Mechanics

A rival to quantum mechanics was published by Schrödinger in the spring of 1926 [1]. It was a new theory, conceived independently of the insights of quantum mechanics and capable of being interpreted in a contrary sense. It was known as Wave Mechanics. It was a very elegant mathematical theory, based physically upon de Broglie's notion of a matter wave associated with every particle and employing in a grand manner that kind of functional analysis developed for electromagnetic theory which was the crowning glory of traditional physics. The new theory immediately fired the imagination of physicists, while Heisenberg's matrix mechanics left them cold. Schrödinger's elegant mathematics was of a kind known to and deeply respected by most physicists: Heisenberg, on the other hand, had been forced to create a new unfamiliar algebra of repelling abstractness. Furthermore, Schrödinger appealed directly to the imaginable qualities of waves, wave packets, of group and phase velocity which were part of the daily currency of classical physics [2]. Compared with the vividness, elegance and pictorial quality of Wave Mechanics, matrix mechanics was, as Schrödinger put it, "von abschreckender ja abstossender Unanschaulichkeit und Abstraktheit" [3]. Bohr straightaway invited Schrödinger to Copenhagen and in the autumn of 1926, Heisenberg and Schrödinger met to discuss their respective viewpoints, with the presence of Bohr as a moderating influence [4].

Heisenberg and Schrödinger

No *rapprochement* occurred between the principals. Heisenberg rejected wave mechanics and Schrödinger rejected quantum mechanics. Heisenberg argued that wave mechanics was incapable of explaining

---

[1] E. Schrödinger, *Ann. d. Physik*, (4) LXXIX (1926), 361; 489; 734; (4) LXXX (1926), 437.
[2] For example, E. Schrödinger described the electron as a small wave packet circulating around the nucleus of an atom in *Naturwissen.*, XIV (1926), p. 664.
[3] Quoted by Heisenberg in *Zeit. f. Physik*, XLIII (1927), p. 195, footnote.
[4] N. Bohr, *Werner Heisenberg* usw., p. x.

quantum discontinuities in the microscopic domain. "The more I think of the physical side of Schrödinger's theory", Heisenberg wrote in the summer of 1926, "the more I find it abhorrent (abscheulich). Schrödinger throws all quantum theory overboard, viz., the photo-electric effect, Franck collisions, the Stern-Gerlack effect, etc. Under these conditions, it is not hard to construct a theory" [1]. Schrödinger rejected equally emphatically, Heisenberg's belief in "quantum jumps" and accused quantum mechanics of being repellingly abstract and unrealistic. Bohr, however, who moderated these discussions, came to the conviction that both theories must be correct since both gave correct results, and urged the adoption of a higher viewpoint in which there was room for both. The name he gave to this higher viewpoint was *complementarity*.

Heisenberg, however, remained firm in the conviction that quantum discontinuities occur in Nature and that they are basic and irreducible data. On 6 November, 1926, the editor of the *Zeitschrift für Physik* received a paper from him entitled "Schwangungerscheinungen und Quantenmechanik", in which he tried to justify this position [2]. He concludes the paper: "A continuous interpretation of the quantum mechanical formalism – and thus also of the de Broglie-Schrödinger wave – does not belong to the substance of these relations. Furthermore, the fact of discontinuities is harmoniously contained in the mathematical scheme of quantum mechanics". The phrase "does not belong to the substance of [quantum or of wave mechanics]" means, in the context, that it cannot be established by *observable criteria*. One would find the conclusion a weak one, if one did not share Heisenberg's master-insight into the nature of physics as a science of observables.

Heisenberg was also stung by Schrödinger's criticisms to defend his theory from the *abstossende Unanschaulichkeit und Abstraktheit* of which it had been accused. During the winter of 1926–1927 Heisenberg and Bohr discussed their different philosophical interpretations of quantum mechanics; Bohr wanting to begin from the acceptance of the complete equivalence of wave and particle pictures, Heisenberg holding to his rejection of wave mechanics and its unverifiable implications of continuity in Nature. Although these discussions took place daily and were often protracted into the night, Heisenberg recounts that "real clarity was not reached", for conflicting conceptual values

[1] Heisenberg, *Erinnerungen* usw., p. 44.
[2] *Zeit. f. Physik*, XL (1927), pp. 501–506.

(*Gedankengut*) were involved. "We could not find our way in all these matters", was his conclusion [1].

Bohr went off to Norway on a skiing holiday in February, 1927, and Heisenberg took the opportunity to elaborate and clarify his own views. These he sent to Pauli who was in substantial agreement with them. Thus originated one of Heisenberg's most celebrated papers, "Ueber den anschaulichen Inhalt der quantentheoretischen Kinematik und Mechanik". It was received by the editor of the *Zeitschrift für Physik* on 23 March, 1927 [2]. When Bohr returned from his holiday and read the manuscript, he still disagreed with Heisenberg's method and starting point. By this time Bohr had elaborated his own interpretation based upon the *Principle of Complementarity*, to which we shall return presently. Heisenberg concluded his account of this period by remarking that, in spite of philosophical differences, the physical consequences of the two interpretations were the same. The note which he added to the manuscript, in deference to Bohr, indicates the possibility of a wave-particle interpretation such as that suggested by Bohr.

SECTION VI: THE INDETERMINACY RELATIONS OF 1927

The Intuitive Meaning of Quantum Mechanics

In the celebrated paper in question, Heisenberg tried to explain what matrix mechanics means to one whose criterion of intelligibility is bound to pictures, images and concrete operations. The dominant idea, as one would expect, is the notion of an observable as dependent on the possibility of measurement. For example, he explains that the concept of place involves a reference to the way position is measured relative to a frame of reference, *"anders hat dieses Wort keinen Sinn"*. Since the position-measurement of a microscopic particle involves the exchange of at least one photon with the measuring instrument, successive position-data for a particle do not lie on a continuous trajectory, but must be represented as it were by a series of separated dots on a graph. These are the observables with which physics starts, and they are *discontinuous*. There is, consequently, no unique rate of change, no unique momentum at a point. There is an average for the short time-interval before the point and a different average generally for the short interval after the point. Hence, exact knowledge of

---

[1] Heisenberg, *Erinnerungen* usw., p. 46, on which this account is based.
[2] *Zeit. f. Physik*, XLIII (1927), pp. 172–198.

position excludes exact knowledge of momentum at that point. This kind of explanation Heisenberg calls the *anschauliche Deutung*, i.e. the *intuitive meaning* of quantum mechanics. It consists in a "qualitative" and in a "theoretical" part, as he says. The theoretical part consists in understanding that the theory is non-contradictory; the qualitative part consists in knowing how the data are experimentally obtained.

The Indeterminacy Relations

Assuming that the position coordinate x of an electron has been measured with a certain degree of accuracy yielding a Gaussian wave packet, Heisenberg then derives the celebrated Indeterminacy (or Uncertainty) Relation:

$$\overline{Dx}.\overline{Dp} \geqq h$$

where $\overline{Dx}$ is the standard deviation of the statistical distribution of x-measurements; $\overline{Dp}$ is the standard deviation of the statistical distribution of p-measurements (where p is the momentum in the x-direction), and h is Planck's constant of action.

All of these points were already *implicit* in Heisenberg's first paper. His discussions with Bohr, and especially his passionate disagreement with Schrödinger's views, forced him to disentangle some of the complex and tangled threads of that notion to which he had given the deceptively simple name of *an observable*. We have already seen that the essential core of meaning of this concept is *measurability*. From the paper we are considering, it becomes clear that, over and above measurability, quantum mechanics is concerned with the properties of *measured concrete data;* that these include necessarily an *interaction with a measuring instrument:* that this interaction is responsible for the *discontinuities* of the data (the so-called quantum jumps), and hence for the *indeterminacy* of the slope between successive data points.

This account has many surprising aspects. In the first place, it is clear that the very same statements can be made of any system, classical or quantum. Successive determinations are always discrete, discontinuous and affected by what are called "instrumental errors". If the classical trajectory is smooth and continuous, it is only because it does not deal directly with concrete data; the smooth curve is a constructed-theoretical norm whose essential property is that concrete data do not diverge from it systematically. It has a definite slope at every point – identified with the classical velocity – only because the curve is an abstraction. Such an ideal path can also be constructed for the quantum mechanical data – it is the plot of expectation values – and coincides in fact with the classical trajectory. This leads to our *first conclusion*, which we have already stated above, that one of the main differences between classical mechanics and quantum mechanics is that the former gives *only* the ideal norm from which concrete data do not systematically diverge; while quantum mechanics gives, in addition, formulae for the way the statistical distributions of concrete data are correlated. In other words, *quantum mechanics unites in a single formalism the functions of both a statistical and a deterministic theory.*

The *second* significant difference between classical and quantum mechanics is in the form of the Indeterminacy Relations. Indeterminacy relations can be constructed in the classical case just as in the case of quantum mechanics, by taking the product of the standard deviations $\overline{Dx}$ and $\overline{Dp}$ of the relative departures of x and p from their classical norms. In the classical case, the probability distributions of Dx and Dp are to be taken as independent, and, unless there is good reason, Gaussian in form. Then $\overline{Dx}$ and $\overline{Dp}$ are independent, and there is no theoretical lower limit to the product $\overline{Dx}.\overline{Dp}$. Of course, if one were to try to make the concrete data more and more precise, one should have passed outside the domain of validity of classical mechanics long before $\overline{Dx}.\overline{Dp}$ has reached the value of h. Quantum mechanics, however, relates the probability distributions of Dx and Dp to one another and establishes that there is a theoretical lower limit of h to the product of their standard deviations.

SECTION VII: THE INDETERMINACY OF THE FACTUAL

Enriching Abstraction

Some idea of the kind of indeterminacy involved in quantum mechanics can be drawn from the preceding account; for if one aspect of quantum mechanics is concerned with concrete data *as such*, then as a corollary there is a certain indeterminacy with regard to the momentary rate of change of the measured variable. It is the *indeterminateness of fact* that follows from our way of knowing; for our first contact with the concrete case is through the presentation of sensible symbols. Such a contact is not yet a knowledge of a thing or an object but merely of a symbol of it. Comparison with other instances leads to an insight which is an understanding of what these sense presentations may possibly symbolise. This insight we called *enriching abstraction*, since it adds to the concrete particularity of the data as not-yet-understood, the enrichment of an act of understanding expressing an ideal norm which is essentially the addition of a set of relations between things or between their symbols. The individual case is then known as a sample of an ideal norm, in so far as it is a member of an ensemble of individual cases which do not systematically diverge from the norm (i.e. which have only random divergence from the norm). However, the indeterminacy of fact is joined with determinacy of definition; for definition is by concept and in this case it is the ideal norm.

In quantum mechanics the definition is represented by the observable as a linear operator implicitly defined within a consistent theory and linked to experimental processes by operational definitions. It answers the question: how is position, momentum, etc., defined? The non-commutation of position and momentum operators becomes part of a new definition (or re-definition vis-à-vis the classical definition) of these which changes the *meaning* (or sense) of *position* and *momentum* for quantum systems [1]. The indeterminacy of fact, however, answers the question: what is the value of the position and momentum coordinates of this system here and now? The answer is given by referring to the results of actual measurements. The indeterminacy of fact is related to the determinacy of definition, as concrete instance is to conceptual definition. What is new in quantum mechanics is not that indeterminacies of variables like position and momentum exist, but that, being formerly thought independent, they are now seen to be related to one another. The measuring process which enters into the definition of one disturbs the measuring-process which enters into the definition of the other. This is the physical significance of the change in *meaning* of "position" and "momentum", accomplished by the quantum mechanical re-definition. Heisenberg then was strictly correct when he said: "Any use of the words 'position' and 'velocity' with an accuracy exceeding that given by [the Indeterminacy Relations] is just as meaningless as the use of words whose sense is not defined" [2].

Ignorance and Nescience

From these considerations there follows our rejection of human ignorance as the basis of probability laws in physics. Human ignorance

---

[1] This point is stressed by N. R. Hanson in *Patterns of Discovery* (Cambridge: 1961), chap. vi, and in *Concept of the Positron* (Cambridge: 1963), chaps. ii-iv. Cf. chap. v, p. 106.
[2] Heisenberg, *Physical Principles* etc., p. 15.

concerns what we could and should know, but do not know. The indeterminacy of the factual, however, which states our inability to increase without limit the number of decimal places in a concrete determination, belongs in the first place to what we *could not* know. Moreover, it is our view that a fully determinate concrete reality is not expressed by an infinity of decimal places. An ideally exact number is a concept and hence performs the function merely of an ideal norm. Finally, we wish to insist that the numbering belongs only to the observable symbol and not directly to the physical property symbolised by it. There may be minds capable of knowing the concrete physical reality in its particularity – perhaps even the human mind in some poetic or mystic mode of operation can reach it – but the particularity would not be expressed through the medium of number sets, it would be a concrete self-revelation of an object in which number possibly has no part. We propose to call our lack of knowledge of concrete factual cases *nescience* instead of ignorance.

Heisenberg does not distinguish between ignorance and nescience, since he, with practically all physicists, shares the view that a concrete case is one which is precisely defined in the sense that all its physical properties possess an infinity of well-determined decimal places. Consequently, the wave packet which describes the probability distribution of the coordinate values is interpreted by him as an expression of the scientist's ignorance of the real physical state of the particle.

Even though it is evident that there is no concrete determination which could not be bettered in some way, we do not agree that the random aspect inescapable from every concrete datum is justly called ignorance. The data on which a particular physical equation is based are neither ideal data nor even the best data – if by "best" one means "with most decimal places" – but merely good data. Good data are data that respect the fact that only a limited number of decimal places are significant in any given physical context and concentrates on these. If a premium is set on the search for more decimal places in every experimental process, a type of unintelligent industry is encouraged which is the stultification of true scientific work. To be called a "master of judicious approximation", as was said of Fermi, does not imply systematic negligence but, on the contrary, excellence of judgement. We do not mean to deny the value of more and more accurate *all-round* experimental measurements, nor do we underestimate the value of more decimal places in the calculation of an ideal norm. What exists, however, is not an ideal norm but a concrete sample in which only a certain number of decimal places are *in fact* significant, and to know how many are significant in fact is a mark of wisdom, and not ignorance[1].

Hence, when Heisenberg states that the dimensions of a wave packet are determined by the subjective conditions of the knower, viz., his ignorance, we reply that, on the contrary, it is determined by the kind of idealization we need to represent the boundary conditions of the experimental context, namely, of the concrete situation. The wave packet is our way of expressing (i) the circumstances under which the system was prepared and (ii) the objective probabilities, viz., the ideal frequencies that arise when subsequent measurements are made upon it. It is not the limitations of our knowledge that specify the wave packet, but it is rather the fact that the physical events can no longer be idealised by deterministic correlations in a purely classical way. Initial boundary conditions no longer determine uniquely (with the appropriate equations) the results of subsequent but otherwise arbitrary measurements that might be made upon the system. A new element has been discovered in the physical situation. Now knowledge has arisen – not on the basis of ignorance as Heisenberg would suggest – but on the basis of a more accurate analysis of the data.

What we have just said points to a certain inconsistency between Heisenberg's principle that observables are the matter of physics and his confused view as to what he thinks physics is *really* about. This last is a relic of the rationalism of classical physics which has not been overcome by the new intentionality implicit in his quantum mechanics of observables.

The Relational Structure of Physical Variables

In describing Heisenberg's view above, we stated that some interaction with a measuring instrument was a necessary consequence of the observability of a physical property. We now ask the question: in Heisenberg's view, is the physical property measured by the observable data *essentially* constituted by the interaction between instrument and object, or is the interaction only an accidental but inescapable means of relating the otherwise imperceptible object to the scientist's experience?

---

[1] Sir Arthur Eddington has rightly said: "By 'observation' we mean *good* observation...; 'good' is not here taken to mean 'perfect'. By *good* observation we emphatically do not mean *perfect* observation... The odd thing is that, having made his perfect arrangements, the perfect observer often fails to accomplish things which to the good observer are quite elementary". *The Philosophy of Physical Science* (Ann Arbor: Univ. of Mich. Press, 1958), pp. 96–97.

If physics is or ought to be concerned only with the way things interact with measuring instruments, then the basic observables of physics are *essentially* constituted as relations between things and things, based upon so many different ways in which things act mutually and reciprocally upon one another. The aim of physics, then, would be to discover interrelated sets of these activities. This would seem to be the logical conclusion of Heisenberg's insight. However, Heisenberg was not able to detach himself sufficiently from the rationalist background of classical physics to draw this conclusion. In failing to do so, he spilled from his sails the guiding breeze of his original inspiration and so never really fully overcame the encircling restrictions of the classical intentionality-structure.

This failure led him to retain a parallelistic theory of knowledge, one different, however, from the naive parallelism characteristic of classical • physics. If the balance illustrates the relational view of physical science then the microscope illustrates the parallelistic theory of science. The balance compares an object in one scale with a standard unit or a fraction of a unit in the other. A microscope on the other hand merely enlarges the impression the object makes on the eye. The classical physicist looked for an exact image of what was out there. Heisenberg accepted this description: the instrument is to man, as he said, rather as a part of our organism than as a part of external nature or as the snail's shell is to its occupant [1]. He pointed out, however, that the instrument through which we look disturbs what is out there and that we see, consequently, not what is there but something which is in part at least a product of the act of observation. "When we speak of the picture of nature in the exact science of our age", he wrote, "we do not mean a picture of nature so much as *a picture of our relationships with nature*" [2].

The Wave Packet

In the paper we have been considering, the notion of a *wave packet* does not emerge clearly. On the one hand, Heisenberg says that, since it results in no more than a probability distribution for the position of the system, it is merely a measure of the scientist's knowledge or lack of knowledge of the physical system. Because of this, he sometimes calls the wave packet a *probability amplitude* or *probability wave*. On the other hand, since this "probability wave" was capable of interfering

---

[1] Heisenberg, *Physicist's Conception* etc., p. 18.
[2] *Ibid.*, p. 29, the author's italics.

with itself like a light wave, he seems also to consider it as more than a mere mathematical function.

His final conclusion is that the probability formulae of quantum mechanics include a reference not only to the kind of experiment which prepared the state, but also to the *kind of experiment which is ultimately envisaged*. By this he means that the development of the wave function does not describe a process occurring independently of observation, but that it represents rather a set of incomplete potentialities which need to be completed by a future act of measurement. He does not discuss here how the probability wave connects past and future states or measurements; this was to be one of the central problems of the new physics. His solution at this stage, in spite of the title of the paper, tends to be abstractly intellectual in keeping with his original insight. The course of our epistemological analysis led us back to the views expressed in this paper. Our own solution was inspired by Heisenberg's original insight and tries to make it consistent with itself and with a satisfactory theory of knowledge.

Summary

In this chapter we discussed how Heisenberg's insight of 1925, that physics should concern itself henceforth only with relations between *observables*, changed the intentionality-structure of physics. This insight led him to the construction of a quantum mechanics of observables. We discussed briefly the significance of his insight and of his rejection of Schrödinger's wave mechanics; the novelty of quantum mechanics as a physical theory, and the meaning he attributed to its most surprising result, viz., the Indeterminacy Relations. We pointed out that the crisis was a crisis of the rationalism inherent in the outlook of classical physics, and that Heisenberg's insistence on "observable quantities" was a return to the individual and empirical manifestations of reality which as such, to our way of knowing, are penetrated with a certain random quality.

CHAPTER THREE

THE INTENTIONALITY STRUCTURE
OF COMPLEMENTARITY

SECTION I: BOHR AND COMPLEMENTARITY

The Copenhagen Spirit

Heisenberg's opposition to wave mechanics did not last long. Influenced by Bohr, he came to accept its elegant mathematical methods – though not Schrödinger's interpretation of them – and also the more concrete manner of presentation afforded by Bohr's *Principle of Complementarity*. In the preface to the lectures he gave at the University of Chicago in the spring of 1929 and published under the title *The Physical Principles of the Quantum Theory*, he speaks of the "conclusive studies of Bohr in 1927" on the nature of the quantum theory, and identifies himself completely with the *Kopenhagener Geist der Quantentheorie* founded, he says, upon the "complete equivalence of corpuscular and wave concepts". "What was born in Copenhagen in 1927", he wrote, "was not only an unambiguous prescription for the interpretation of experiments, but also a language in which one spoke about Nature on the atomic scale, and in so far a part of philosophy" [1]. Heisenberg's acceptance of wave mechanics as an intrinsic part of the quantum theory was understandable; but his capitulation to the philosophy of complementarity was, in our opinion, unfortunate; for it led him away from the true sense of his original insight [2].

---

[1] W. Heisenberg, "The Development of the Interpretation of the Quantum Theory" in *Niels Bohr and the Development of Physics*, ed. by W. Pauli (Oxford: Pergamon Press, 1955), p. 16.

[2] It is often said and generally believed that the quantum theory owes its origin and inspiration to the spirit of complementarity. On this point, P. K. Feyerabend writes not altogether unjustly: "The full quantum theory we owe to a metaphysics diametrically opposed to the philosophical point of view of Niels Bohr and his disciples, viz., to that of Schrödinger. This is quite an important historical fact as the adherents of the Copenhagen picture very often criticize the metaphysics of Bohm and Vigier by pointing out that no *physical theory* has yet been developed on the basis... They forget that the Copenhagen way of thinking *has not produced a theory either*. What it *has* produced is the proper interpretation of Schrödinger's wave mechanics after this theory has been introduced. For it turned out that Schrödinger's

Complementarity

The Principle of Complementarity is not a physical principle like the the Indeterminacy Principle, nor is it a heuristic principle in physics like the Correspondence Principle; but it is a philosophical (or epistemological) principle which attempts to explain how we know the atomic domain and how the inherent limitations of our knowing powers impede our conception and expression of the intrinsic nature of micro-physical events [1].

In the seven paragraphs immediately following we give our summary of the philosophy of complementarity with some comments on the import of the doctrines involved.

(i) The aim of atomic physics is to put order into an increasing range of our experiences with a view to predicting patterns in these experiences [2]. The Galilean and Newtonian aim of trying to find out the truth about the heavens and the earth is to be abandoned for the reason alleged by Bohr that the interior resources we have for investigating the atomic domain are too modest to allow us ever to reach such a truth.

(ii) The resources of our knowing powers are limited by the "forms of perception" [3] which allow us to speak and to describe only (what we have called) *bodies in the strict sense,* and to conceive only inductive generalisations of bodily phenomena. The two kinds of bodies are particles which are localisable and fields which are non-localisable,

wave mechanics was just that complete rational generalisation of the classical theory that Bohr, Heisenberg and their collaborators had been looking for and parts of which they had already succeeded in developing", in "Problems in Microphysics", *Frontiers of Science and Philosophy* (London: Allen and Unwin, 1964), pp. 264–266.

[1] References will be made chiefly to the following works of N. Bohr: *Atomic Theory and the Description of Nature* (Cambridge: 1961), which is a collection of four of Bohr's most celebrated articles on the interpretation of quantum mechanics published originally between 1925 and 1929, with an introductory survey and commentary by the author written in 1934; "Can Quantum Mechanical Description of Physical Reality be Complete?", *Phys. Rev.,* XLVIII (1936), 696; "On the Notions of Causality and Complementarity", *Dialectica,* 7/8 (1948), pp. 312–319; "Discussions with Einstein on Epistemological Problems in Atomic Theory", in *Albert Einstein: Philosopher-Scientist,* pp. 199–242. For a detailed study of Bohr's philosophy of complementarity by a modern philosopher-physicist, cf., P. K. Feyerabend, "Complementarity", in *Proc. Aristot. Soc., Suppl. Vol.,* XXXII (1958), pp. 75–104. It should be noted that the philosophical doctrine called *Complementarity* has undergone considerable evolution, notably on the part of Heisenberg and in a sense away from the predominantly empiricist spirit of the early phase. For the essentials of what might be called the *irreducible physical principles* of complementarity, see *Concept of the Positron,* chaps. VI–VII, by N. R. Hanson. It is in the sense of Hanson that most physicists belong to the Copenhagen School. However, there is a big difference between Hanson's summary and the unabridged philosophies of Bohr and Heisenberg.

[2] Bohr, *Atomic Theory* etc., pp. 1, 12, 16–17, 55, 69, 77, 87.

[3] *Ibid.,* pp. 1, 5, 15–19, 22, 90–93, 96, 103, 111; *Albert Einstein,* etc., pp. 209; *Dialectica,* p. 313; *Phys. Rev., loc. cit.,* p. 702.

although a field may give rise to a wave packet of virtually finite dimensions. Thus, the forms of perception "idealise" every experience and notably those of atomic phenomena by submitting them to a synthesis in which the velocity of light is represented as infinitely large, and Planck's constant is represented as vanishingly small [1]. In other words, every experience of atomic phenomena is "idealised" *either* as a particle *or* as a wave. This is what is meant by *wave-particle duality*. This idealisation, however, is due to our forms of perception and is neither a coherent objective picture of the atomic event taken as a phenomenon nor does it give us true knowledge of the atomic event as a reality [2]. Bohr was a realist in the empiricist sense; that is, he held that reality, if it is to be known truly, can be known only in and through a stable and coherent phenomenal object. Since no coherent phenomenal object can be formed of an atomic event, he considered that the atomic event cannot be known as a reality, that is, as it is in itself.

(iii) The concepts of quantum mechanics are defined in terms of the concepts of classical physics. These are just refinements of the concepts of everyday life and refer only to bodies in the strict sense [3].

(iv) Our experience of atomic phenomena occurs within acts of observation. These involve a union between the knowing subject and the known object in which no sharp distinction can be made between them. Moreover, the observing subject disturbs its object in the act of observing it: the disturbance of macroscopic objects is very small, but in the atomic domain the disturbance is considerable and, moreover, inescapable, since the subject and the object must share between them at least one indivisible quantum of energy [4]. Hence, our (private) subjectivity enters essentially and inevitably into our experience of atomic phenomena. This theory of observation is founded upon what we shall call the *perturbation theory of measurement*. This completes the two aspects under which our knowledge is *non-objective*. (The first was mentioned above in (ii).

(v) A consequence of this is that (bodily or phenomenal) causality does not hold for atomic phenomena. Hence the statistical laws of the atomic domain are irreducible [5]. *Bodily* (or *phenomenal*) *causality*, it

<hr />

[1] Bohr, *Atomic Theory* etc., pp 5, 16–17, 22, 66, 116.

[2] *Ibid.*, pp. 1, 5, 96–97, 116.

[3] *Ibid.*, pp. 1, 5, 8, 17, 53.

[4] *Ibid.*, pp. 1, 4–5, 10–11, 22, 53–54, 67, 93–96, 114, 119; *Albert Einstein etc.*, pp. 224; *Dial.*, *loc. cit.*, pp. 313, 317.

[5] Bohr, *Atomic Theory* etc., pp. 4, 5, 13, 57–61, 117.

will be remembered, is the law-like association in a continuous temporal sequence of spatially organised bodies (or phenomena).

(vi) The function of mathematical theory is not merely to be an "indispensable tool for describing quantitative relationships", like Heisenberg's matrix mechanics, it is also "an essential means for the elucidation of the general qualitative points of view" [1], that is, it can also be used to describe the two complementary viewpoints represented by the wave and particle pictures.

(vii) The *"reduction (or contraction) of the wave packet"* which is the name given to what takes place in an act of observation, is partly a *physical effect* since it results from the physical union of subject and object. It is partly a *psychological effect* in so far as the subject translates this uniquely into a psychological act of observation: this translation takes place according to the *Principle of Psycho-physical Parallelism* [2]. And it is partly a *logical effect*, since, as Feyerabend points out [3], the subject switches suddenly from a wave-type or field-type description to a particle-type description.

The way of complementarity then consists in "liberalising" our classical concepts [4]. This means knowing when to use a particle representation and when to use a field or wave-like representation to order our experiences. Every statement of fact in the quantum theory is necessarily a statement in terms of classical concepts, that is, in terms of the concepts of classical particle physics and in terms of the concepts of classical field physics. As Reichenbach has well said of the duality of wave and particle: "The *and* is not in the language of physics, but in the *metalanguage*, that is in a language which speaks about the language of physics... It does not refer to the physical object but to possible descriptions of the physical object and thus falls into the realm of the philosopher" [5].

The kind of physical theory based upon complementarity is called by Bohr a "rational generalization of classical physics" [6]. The *Correspondence Principle* is, accordingly, a kind of transcendental deduction from the Principle of Complementarity [7].

[1] *Ibid.*, p. 8.
[2] *Ibid.*, pp. 24, 118; cf., *infra*, chap. IV.
[3] Feyerabend, *loc. cit.*, p. 95.
[4] Bohr, *Atomic Theory* etc., pp. 3, 5, 18, 63.
[5] Hans Reichenbach, *Rise of Scientific Philosophy*, (Berkeley: Univ. of Cal. Press, 1962), pp. 175–176.
[6] Bohr, *Atomic Theory* etc., pp. 4, 19, 70, 87, 92, 110; *Dial., loc. cit.*, p. 316; *Albert Einstein* etc., pp. 210, 239.
[7] Bohr, *Atomic Theory* etc., pp. 37, 70, 86, 110; cf., *infra*, chap. VI.

SECTION II: HEISENBERG AND COMPLEMENTARITY

Heisenberg and Complementarity

That his acceptance of complementarity made Heisenberg vaguely uneasy at the beginning is suggested by the account he wrote in 1960, and to which we have frequently referred [1]. In this he goes out of his way to note that he preferred a different approach to quantum mechanics from Bohr's. Not only was there the question of discontinuities in nature, but their viewpoints and casts of mind were different. Bohr's approach to physics was empirical, and moved from the phenomena to theory, which he considered to be a movement from a lesser generalisation to a greater one; Heisenberg on the other hand took a more intellectualistic approach to physics, moving from the potentialities of theory to the testing of these in phenomena [2]. Bohr could be classified as empiricist and positivist in his metaphysics; while Heisenberg on the other hand was, and became increasingly with the lapse of time, an idealist. Both, however, called themselves realists; but for different reasons; Bohr because for him the reality of everyday life (and classical physics) was the *really real* which he understood in an empiricist sense, while Heisenberg called himself a realist because he never lost sight of the transcendent object which, though unknowable, was the noumenal correlate of the phenomena. This difference in viewpoint showed up in their different interpretations of the Indeterminacy Relations: as Landé put it; Bohr affirmed the *Unschärfe des Seins*, while Heisenberg asserted merely the *Unbestimmtheit der Voraussage* [3]. It was only because they could agree in their interpretation of the phenomenal plane that Heisenberg could with sincerity accept the premises of complementarity. However, while complementarity constituted the whole horizon of Bohr's philosophy, it was really only an element – let us say, a premise – for the gradual elaboration of Heisenberg's metaphysics. In starting point, in problematic and in systematic conclusions, Heisenberg played Kant to Bohr's Hume.

Wave-particle Duality in Heisenberg

In the *Physical Principles of the Quantum Theory*, Heisenberg paid tribute to the "conclusive studies of Bohr" and dedicated his work to

[1] Heisenberg, *Erinnerungen* usw.
[2] Heisenberg, *Niels Bohr* etc., pp. 12–29, especially p. 15.
[3] A. Landé, "Dualismus, Wissenschaft und Hypothese", in *Werner Heisenberg und die Physik unserer Zeit*, p. 124.

the "diffusion of the *Kopenhagener Geist der Quantentheorie*... which has directed the entire development of modern physics [1].

All our concepts, he says, are attempts to "clarify and synthesise results" [2] which are described in classical concepts, i.e., in the "language of everyday life" [3]. These concepts are idealisations in which "both the gravitational constant and the reciprocal of the velocity of light may be regarded as negligibly small" [4]. They refer exclusively to things of which we can form a picture in the imagination [5]. All our concepts, except mathematical concepts, are formed by inductive generalisations of experience, but the limits of their applicability are to be determined by reference to experience [6]. Particle and wave properties of both light and matter, which are intimately linked in experiment, are too different to be simultaneous properties of the same thing. Hence, we are led to form "two mental pictures – one of a particle and the other of waves – both incomplete". They are complementary and mutually exclusive aspects of atomic phenomena. Each has a limited domain of applicability and neither must be "pushed too far" [7]. When we speak, we refer to one or other of these pictures, but neither is a true visualisation of the atomic event. Atomic phenomena cannot be explained as relations between objects existing in space and time [8]. Consequently, our knowledge of events is an inextricable mixture of subjective and objective elements [9].

A traditional requirement of science has been a sharp division between subject and object, i.e. between observer and observed [10]. This is possible in classical physics where the interaction between them is negligible [11]. In the atomic domain, however, the interaction can cause "uncontrollable and large changes in the system observed" [12]. The union between the observer and the observed is such that it is impossible to determine what part of a system belongs to one and what part to the other [13]. This leads to a certain inescapable indetermincay in our knowledge of the simultaneous values of certain quantities,

---

[1] Heisenberg's Preface to *Physical Principles of the Quantum Theory*.
[2] Heisenberg, *Physical Principles* etc., p. 1.
[3] *Ibid.*, pp. 1–3.
[4] *Ibid.*, p. 2.
[5] *Ibid.*, p. 11.
[6] *Ibid.*, pp. 1, 11.
[7] *Ibid.*, pp. 10, 64, chaps. ii and iii.
[8] *Ibid.*, pp. 63–64.
[9] *Ibid.*, p. 65 and *passim*.
[10] *Ibid.*, p. 2.
[11] *Ibid.*, p. 3.
[12] *Ibid.*, pp. 3, 64, 20–46.
[13] *Ibid.*, pp. 58, 64, 67.

which is expressed in the Indeterminacy Relations [1]. This indeterminateness is attached to our knowledge of each individual microscopic
object [2]. Our knowledge then of this class of objects is limited to
irreducible statistical distributions and correlations [3].

Causality in Heisenberg

The Principle of Causality expressed in the form "Natural phenomena obey exact laws" is to be renounced. Causality, he says, can
be defined only for an isolated system [4]. No set of atomic systems, in
so far as they are the objects of observation-acts, obeys the law of
causality, since the act of observation disturbs them, and this disturbance precludes the exact geometrical description of each which is
a necessary condition for causality [5]. The disturbance is due to the
sharing of ultimate and indivisible entities (viz., quanta of energy) [6].
The influence of the measuring device which brings about a discontinuous change in the system "is treated in a different manner from
the interaction of the various parts of the system"; these on the other
hand enter determinately and causally into the description [7]. The
discontinuance change produced by an act of measurement is called the
"reduction of the wave packet". It is a physical effect since it effects
a change in the object [8]. It is a psychological effect since it results in a
discontinuous change in our knowledge [9]. It is a logical effect since it
results in a change of the mathematical representation of the physical
process from a wave to a particle picture [10].

Heisenberg has reaffirmed all the propositions of this section and of
the preceding one many times since 1929, and he has given more detailed
and explicit treatment of some of the key ideas. For example in 1931,
he gave a conference to a group of physicists and philosophers in which
he described the crisis produced in the concept of causality and in the
Law of Causality by quantum mechanics. Most of the members of the

---

[1] *Ibid.*, pp. 13–46.
[2] *Ibid.*, pp. 2,2 52.
[3] *Ibid.*, pp. 33–34, and *passim*.
[4] *Ibid.*, pp. 62 -63. Note that Heisenberg often uses the term "causality" in a wider sense
than Bohr, as referring to any determinate connection parametrised by time between
entities, whether these be mathematical, phenomenal or bodily entities.
[5] *Ibid.*, pp. 58, 63 and *passim*.
[6] *Ibid.*, p. 63.
[7] *Ibid.*, p. 58. Note that this implies a *perturbation theory of measurement*, viz., that the
measured object is disturbed by the measurement and its true properties thereby obscured
by it.
[8] *Ibid.*, p. 39 and *passim*.
[9] *Ibid.*, p. 36 and *passim*.
[10] *Ibid.*, p. 36.

group, like J. von Neumann, P. Frank and H. Reichenbach, belonged to the Vienna Circle. The conference was published in *Erkenntnis* under the title *"Kausalgesetz und Quantentheorie"* [1].

In this conference, Heisenberg examines five different formulations of the Law of Causality and finds them either tautologous, not falsifiable or *inhaltsleer*. A formulation is tautologous if it merely analyses the sense of the words without affirming the existence of a referent for this sense. A non-falsifiable proposition is one whose referents, if there are such, are inaccessible to human investigation. A concept is *inhaltsleer* if it has no referent, that is, if there is nothing in fact in which it is verified. A law is *inhaltsleer* if it has no observable consequences [2]. The sense of *inhaltsleer* corresponds to the positivist notion of *ohne Bedeutung* (often translated by meaningless).

Heisenberg finds that the classical Law of Causality (viz., that characteristic of classical physics) is *inhaltsleer* (presumably in atomic physics only), since the conditions of applicability of its concepts and hence of the law are never fulfilled. The classical law of causality can be formulated: "In an isolated system, if the present state of the system is known in all its particulars, then the future state of the system can be calculated". Heisenberg points out that an isolated system is an *unobserved system*, since the act of observation would result in a fusion of the system with a knowing subject, thus removing its isolation as well as disturbing its original state. Moreover, since the Uncertainty Principle does not permit exact knowledge of all the variables of the initial state of the system, the conditions for the fulfilment of the classical physical law of causality are never in fact fulfilled. He considers the substitution of "ray in Hilbert space" (or "wave function") for the "present state of the system" and notes that the Schrödinger equation describes deterministically the time-change of this ray (or wave function). This species of causality, he says, is not real causality since the space of the wave function is *configuration space* (i.e., an abstract theoretical $3n$-dimensional space – where n is the number of particles) and not the space of observable events [3]. Ob-

---

[1] Heisenberg, *Erkenntnis, loc. cit.*

[2] *Ibid.,* p. 173.

[3] Heisenberg distinguishes between two kinds of waves: the "configuration space wave" which is also the wave function of a many particle system, and the "probability wave" or the "wave packet". The former is an ideal mathematical construction in a space of $3n$-dimensions (cf., *Physical Principles* etc., Preface; *Philosophic Problems* etc., p. 15). The latter is the three-dimensional matter wave associated with the complementary particle picture. Within the perspective of complementarity, the "probability wave" has as much "reality" as the particle, i.e., both are equivalent ways of speaking about the same physical object; cf., *Niels Bohr* etc., p. 24; *Physical Principles* etc., p. 13.

servable events are not connected causally, but – except in the case of commuting operators – only statistically. Nor is there any escape from indeterminism by including the observer (i.e. the eyes and the other senses of the scientist as well as his instruments) within the system in order to construct a more inclusive but isolated system of which the observer is now a part; for this just leads to a more comprehensive wave function which has in turn to be *reduced* to one of the possibilities it contains by some super-act of observation. There is no way, he concludes, of setting up or predicting a determinate chain of observable events in quantum mechanics.

Of the Kantian expression of the Law of Causality, viz., that there is a unique antecedent-consequent connection between objectifiable events, Heisenberg concludes that it too is *inhaltsleer*, since atomic events – because of the Indeterminacy Principle – cannot be objectified in the Kantian sense. He compares the status of the Law of Causality with the principles of Euclidean geometry. Both are synthetic *a priori* principles according to Kant. Since Einstein's relativity theory has shown that a gravitational field is characterised by a non-Euclidean geometry, we are justified in saying only that space is Euclidean, *if* the conditions for the fulfilment Euclidean geometry are fulfilled. This last is an *a posteriori* condition and might not in fact be fulfilled, or might be fulfilled only in certain cases. Similarly, with the Kantian Law of Causality, the conditions for its application might not be fulfilled and are not in fact fulfilled in atomic physics. Since Kant has shown that the Law of Causality is a necessary condition for *objective* science, he concludes that quantum mechanics is not objective. The objectivity in question is that attributed by Kant to all empirical scientific objects. This is (what we have called) *phenomenal objectivity*. The non-objectivity of a quantum system is shown by the fact that it is known only to the extent that it interacts with an observer-subject. Heisenberg concludes from this that modern physics is not concerned with the essence and structure of the atom but with observable events. The emphasis is thus placed upon the measurement process. He adds as an afterthought that, although the Law of Causality is no longer universal, causality holds between successive repetitions of a measurement since these give the same (or neighbouring) values for the measured quantity.

During the course of the subsequent discussion, he asked whether, in the reduction of the wave packet, the selection of one observed value out of the many possible values is to be explained by the physiology of the human observer. He replies that a photographic plate can play the part of an observer equally well: "aber das ist noch kein Zusammenhang zwischen der Physik und psychologischen Fragen" [1]. It is doubtful whether, given the later development of measurement theory along the lines suggested by complementarity, he would give the same answer to-day.

In a reply to von Neumann, he puts on record his opposition to any way of speaking which would identify the wave function with the *Ding an sich*. In the later development of his thought, he would affirm a *Ding an sich* represented by the wave function, to which he would give the name *potentia* or *objektive Tendenz* [2].

Heisenberg's View of Physics

Heisenberg's *Principielle Fragen der Modernen Physik* (1936) and his *Wandlungen in den Grundlagen der Naturwissenschaft* (8th edition, 1949) which are collections of occasional lectures delivered between 1932 and 1948, restate without change or development the propositions we have enunciated above [3]. In these lectures, Heisenberg shows himself interested in the historical and dialectical development of the concept of nature from the Middle Ages up to the present day [4]. He sees himself justly in the line of those who helped to change man's view of nature and, reflexively, his view of himself vis-à-vis nature.

We have pointed out that Heisenberg's approach to physics was from the starting point of theory, i.e., from the free creative uninhibited search for mathematical theories *a priori* to external empirical experience. These played the part of Kant's pure science of nature, not to the extent that they laid down absolute and necessary conditions of possibility which every scientific object obeys, but to the extent that they served to define conditions of possibility for *possible* scientific objects. A theory which is *inhaltsleer* is distinguished from one which has observable consequences by having recourse to empirical tests [5]. He held that neither the forms of thought, nor experience itself imposed on us a unique *a priori* or pure science of nature. The representative value and the limits of applicability of each theory were to be de-

---

[1] *Ibid.*, p. 184.

[2] See *infra*, chap. VIII, pp. 150–2.

[3] These two volumes have been translated into English and appear together under the title: *Philosophic Problems of Nuclear Physics* (London: Faber and Faber, 1952).

[4] *Ibid.*, pp. 12–13; also W. Heisenberg, "Der Begriff 'Abgeschlossene Theorie' in der modernen Naturwissenschaft", *Dialectica*, II, 7/8 (1948), pp. 331–336.

[5] Heisenberg, *Physical Principles* etc., p. 15.

termined *a posteriori* by experimental investigation [1]. In this respect, he abandoned both the rationalisitc intentionality-structure of classical physics, and the rigid set of synthetic *a priori* principles which Kant alleged were necessarily operative in the construction of every scientific object. A theory verified within a limited domain was given the name *"abgeschlossene Theorie"* (a *Closed* or *Complete Theory*) [2]. Heisenberg gave four examples: (a) Newtonian Mechanics, (b) Maxwell's electromagnetic theory, (c) heat and statistical mechanics, and (d) the quantum theory with chemistry annexed. We shall return to the notion of a Closed (or Complete) Theory later on.

In a paper entitled *Wahrscheinlichkeitsaussagen in der Quantentheorie der Wellenfelder* (1938) [3], Heisenberg again reiterates his view that the act of measurement disturbs the object and thereby sets limits to our knowledge; that such knowledge as we are capable of, is penetrated with an inescapable (private) subjectivity; and that, consequent on the inter-penetration of subject and object in physics, the laws of atomic physics are irreducibly probabilistic.

This account brings us approximately up to the year 1950. As the subsequent development of his philosophy concerned principally the ontology of nature, we shall postpone the consideration of his later works of philosophical interest to Part II. We shall summarise below some of the principles and conclusions of Heisenberg's philosophy with regard to scientific method and the structure of knowledge. Our criticism of these will occupy the next three chapters.

SECTION III:

THE   INTENTIONALITY   STRUCTURE   OF   COMPLEMENTARITY

Complementarity in its original form contains two key ideas on *scientific method* and three basic propositions in *philosophy*. The two sets of ideas are intimately related and constitute a logical whole which we might call the *intentionality-structure* of complementarity in its early phase.

The key propositions on scientific method are the following: (1) The definition of variables can only be made with the aid of classical physical concepts. These are identical – except for refinements

---

[1] Heisenberg, *Philosophic Problems* etc., p. 23; and *Zeit. f. Physik*, XLIII (1927), p. 172.
[2] Heisenberg, *Philosophic Problems* etc., p. 24; and *Dial.*, *loc. cit.*, pp. 331–336.
[3] W. Heisenberg, "Wahrscheinlichkeitsaussagen in der Quantentheorie der Wellenfelder", *Actualités scientifiques et industrielles*, No. 734 (Paris: Hermann, 1938).

– with the concepts of everyday life; (2) The act of measurement perturbs the object. Its objective state ("objective" that is, "not affected by the subjectivity of purely private experience") cannot be known – whether as an object of empirical science (a phenomenal object) or as a reality (an object in the strict or formal sense). The Indeterminacy Principle expresses the degree of this perturbation, and, at the same time, traces the limits of our power of knowing physical objects. We call this the *perturbation theory of measurement*.

Three basic philosophical propositions are linked with these [1]. (i) It is impossible for us to know atomic events in their transcendent noumenal reality or in an objectifiable phenomenal reality, since the resources of our knowing powers are limited to manipulating and synthesising phenomenal representations. Two kinds of phenomenal representations are available to us, wave representations and particle representations, and out of these our knowledge of atomic systems has to be constructed. The resulting construction lacks both formal (or strict) objectivity and empirical objectivity. (2) Causality (viz., the strict temporal antecedent-consequent link between bodies or phenomena) fails in atomic physics and for this reason atomic systems are not empirically objectifiable, and for the same reason the statistical laws of quantum physics are irreducible. (3) The only knowledge which has a right to be called *objective knowledge of physical reality* is an observation-event: this is the perception of an everyday event occurring in (three-demensional) space and ordinary time. With regard to atomic systems, our knowledge is not objective – even in the sense of public objectivity. We know such systems only in an observation-event which is the indissoluble union of observer (subject) and observed (object) and to such knowledge is attached an irreducible element of the subjectivity of private experience. Quantum mechanics may be said to have a public instrumental value or public objectivity only for the purpose of (statistical) prediction or technical use. As far as individual systems are concerned, our knowledge falls short even of public objectivity.

Summary

The return to the concrete and empirical implied in Heisenberg's insight on the importance of *observables* in physics was not, however,

[1] The philosophical propositions outlined below belong to a phase which lasted in Heisenberg's case up to approximately 1950. After that, the predominantly rationalist and Kantian bent of his mind separated him more and more from Bohr and the empiricist wing of the Copenhagen School. A comparison will be made in Part II between Heisenberg's early and late philosophy.

in Heisenberg's case, accompanied by a thorough re-thinking of the rationalist presuppositions of classical physics. The effect on Bohr, however, was to lead him to a complete rejection of rationalism and to the adoption of the contrary extreme, empiricism. The profound – though largely implicit – cause of the disagreement between Bohr and Heisenberg as to the correct interpretation of quantum mechanics, was resolved in the summer of 1927, by the common acceptance of the philosophy of complementarity. This was based upon the acceptance of wave mechanics – though not of Schrödinger's interpretation of it – as an equally valid part of the quantum theory with matrix mechanics. A corollary of this was agreement about the complete equivalence of wave and particle representations of quantum phenomena. The latter was called *wave-particle dualism* or the *Principle of Complementarity*. The common acceptance of complementarity resulted in agreement as to the language in which quantum phenomena were to be described. In this chapter, we stated the essential propositions of the philosophy of complementarity concerning the nature and limits of human knowing, scientific method and the ontology of nature.

CHAPTER FOUR

COMPLEMENTARITY
AND THE SCIENTIFIC METHOD: A CRITICISM

SECTION I: PROPOSITION (I) ON SCIENTIFIC METHOD

Proposition (1)

The definition of quantum mechanical variables can only be made with the aid of classical physical concepts. These are identical – except for refinements – with the concepts of everyday life. Heisenberg has written: "The concepts of classical physics will remain the basis of any exact and objective science. Because we demand of the results of science that they can be objectively proved (i.e. by measurements, registered on suitable apparatus) we are forced to express these results in the language of classical physics... Thus while the *laws* of classical physics... appear only as limiting cases of more general and abstract connections, the *concepts* associated with these laws remain an indispensable part of the language of science without which it would not be possible even to speak of scientific results" [1].

Criticism

We contend that there are two logically distinct sets of concepts in physics, whether in classical or in quantum physics; and that failure to advert to this vitiates the above proposition. We attribute such failure to a theory of knowledge implicit in the philosophy of complementarity, a theory which is usually given the name *psycho-physical parallelism*. As psycho-physical parallelism is the key to the philosophic thinking of many physicists to-day, we shall devote the following paragraphs to it.

Psycho-physical Parallelism

The intentionality-structure of classical physics implied a naive Cartesian Dualism of Mind and Body. In its original form, Cartesian

---

[1] Heisenberg, *Philosophic Problems* etc., p. 45; the same idea is expressed in the same author's *Physics and Philosophy* (New York: Harper, 1958), pp. 44, 144.

Dualism regarded the knowing subject as "mirroring" the known object (its referent), and the accuracy of the representation was guaranteed by the veracity of God. Under the influence of the Kantian critique, this dualism was transformed into a parallelism and was introduced into the interpretation of modern physics by Bohr [1]. His psycho-physical parallelism postulates a unique "translation" of physical events into psychic acts of observation (called "sensations") [2]. Science, then, concerns itself with the organisation of these "sensations" on the empirical level, and with the construction of theoretical entities (theoretical constructs) to give them a coherent ground in a unified consciousness. Whether the "sensations" were given an empiricist or idealistic interpretation, the core idea was the same, namely, an isomorphism between the content of conscious acts of observation (the sensations) and the unconscious physical events which they express and which are their underlying cause. The function of mind called sensation *models* physical events – not in the naive realistic way of Cartesian Dualism which was based upon the isomorphism of (idealised) bodies imaginatively represented with the external world – but only in *observation events* (*Beobachtungsvorgänge*). Only observation-events express knowledge of physical reality. Physical reality is, by definition, expressed by the type of sensations called "observation-events". A scientific observation-event is one accomplished with the aid of instruments.

Implicit in this view are two propositions about the nature of scientific method: (a) a physical property is the *direct* physical correlate of the empirical content of a scientific observation-event. In other words, the act of observation *translates* the appropriate physical property into the empirical content of a conscious act; that is, just as "physical colour" is related to "colour-as-sensed", and "physical shape" is related to "shape-as-seen", so a "physical property" is related to the "property-as-observed in the scientific observation-event". This

---

[1] The Principle of Psycho-physical Parallelism was first expressed by G. Th. Fechner, and it influenced the interpretation of physics through Wilhelm Ostwald's *Lectures in Natural Philosophy*. Extracts from Ostwald's lectures are included in Heisenberg's collection: "The Origins of the Mechanistic and Materialist World-View", *Physicist's Conception of Nature*, pp. 137–151. (Although Heisenberg's name is on the book-cover, it is not clear that he was also the compiler of the extracts. The extracts at any rate have a value of their own).

[2] N. Bohr, *Naturwissen.*, xvii (1929); translated and published under the title "The Atomic Theory and the Fundamental Principles of the Description of Nature", in *Atomic Theory and the Description of Nature*, pp. 102–119. The first systematic use of the principle in the quantum theory of measurement was made by J. von Neumann in *Mathematische Grundlagen der Quantenmechanik*, (Berlin: Springer, 1932). In the English trans. by R. T. Beyer, *Mathematical Foundations of Quantum Mechanics*, it is stated on p. 420.

implies that there is *no logical difference* in structure between the way we express a physical property in a scientific concept and the way we express an everyday property in an everyday concept. (b) Between the use of everyday (pre-scientific) concepts and the use of scientific concepts there is the difference that in science the *intervention of instruments* occurs. These enable publicly objective comparisons to be made and verified by different people and add a new exactness of expression to the concepts through the use of mathematical relationships. They also perform the functions of filtering out unwanted elements in a complex situation, of magnifying those we want, or of "translating" them into new forms which our powers of perception can better recognise and deal with. Useful and in fact indispensable as these instruments are in physics, this view holds that they really come between the physicist and the physical object, and, if the physical object is very small, the presence of the instrument disturbs it. According to this theory, which we called the *perturbation theory of measurement*, the principal discovery of quantum mechanics is the essential limitation of physical instruments to reveal very small objects as they really are.

The second assertion (b) above will be considered fully in the next section. In reply to the first assertion (a), we distinguish between two classes of concepts. One has a logical structure based upon the resemblances of things as regards their appearance to us and the uses they have in the practical affairs of life. These are *descriptive concepts*, based upon thing-to-us relations, and they describe a World of things and properties which are *for-us*. These are the *concepts of everyday life*, enlarged and specialised so as to be able to describe experimental procedures (*operational concepts*) and experimental results (*observational concepts*).

The other class of concepts has a logical structure based upon resemblances as regards the mutual interactivity of things. They are *explanatory concepts*, founded upon thing-to-thing relations and they describe a World of things *for-things* and of properties *for-things*, notably for that class of things which can serve our purpose as measuring instruments [1]. The resemblances on which these concepts are based

---

[1] The expression *World-for-things* does not connote that an observer-instrument (which is the *thing* in the *World-for-things*) has a consciousness like a human observer open to a horizon of reality called a *World*. Reality is known only by a human observer. But just as everyday realities are known within a World-structure which is a set of relations *to the knower*, so we state that scientific realities are known within a World-context of a set of relations centered on things (or observer-instruments). One might take the expression "World-for-things" to be shorthand for "World-of-things-to-things-for-us". See below, chapter VII.

cannot be known *directly*, since they do not concern how things look or appear to us. They can only be *inferred* from their effects in nature and in the controlled environment of the laboratory. These effects are *sensible signs* or *observable symbols* which, when interpreted correctly, reveal a network of related activities among things. Since a physical theory is the expression of an insight into such a set of interrelated activities, an act of observation is not simply the translation into consciousness of a physical event. It is the perception of a sensible event and, with it, the recognition that it is endowed with a symbolism revealing something which is not *per se* sensible, since it is neither a thing-for-us nor a property-for-us, but a thing-for-things or a property-for-things. As a consequence, the function of a measuring instrument – which is the term of such relations – is not just to bring a degree of exactness and public objectivity into science which everyday knowledge lacks, but to help to create a new kind of knowledge, based upon a new kind of concept, expressing a new kind of relation. Just as the observed effects of a physical property are known only through observable symbols, like pointer readings, etc., so the mind can deal with these properties only through a constructed mathematical symbolism which symbolises in turn these observed effects and which, through its mathematical form, reveals the essential, relational structure of the symbolised properties.

A physical property or variable, then, is expressed by us as the union of two concepts – an *explanatory concept* [1] and an *operational concept*. The explanatory concept draws its intelligibility from a systematic totality which in the concrete is a sphere of reality to which we give the name *World-for-things* and is the *sphere of the scientific real*. Operational concepts and observational concepts draw their intelligibility from a systematic totality which in the concrete is the sphere of the everyday real which is called the *World-for-us*. Each World has its own symbolic embodiment in a language; the *observation language* of the World-for-us and the *explanatory language* of the World-for-things, which are linked by their common denotation [2]. The linguistic link between the two languages is called a *correspondence rule*.

We stress the operational aspect of physical properties, since it is by certain activities on our part that we produce the controlled environment in which things interact among themselves in such a way as to ground a *single* thing-to-thing relation and a single property. But we

---

[1] See *supra*, pp. 14, 59.
[2] *Infra*, chap. x.

do not say, as Bridgman and the advocates of *operationalism* say, that the physical concept is no more than a generalised set of procedures to be performed by us. The physical concept *explains* the procedures, that is, it gives the reason why they measure one single property (and not a mixture of properties). It also explains why the set of measuring devices for a single property is an open set.

A Pseudo-problem

The distinctions we have just made belong to physical (or scientific) method in so far as this is a human way of investigating reality. From the failure to distinguish the human element in physics from its proper object, many pseudo-scientific problems arise. Complementarity, for instance, fails to recognise the difference in logical structure between physical concepts and the concepts of everyday life, and consequently overlooks the difference between the observable symbol which is an event in everyday life and the physical thing or property which is essentially unrepresentable in observational concepts. This gives rise to a series of pseudo-scientific problems based upon the dilemma: Is a quantum system a wave or a particle? In chapter v we explain our reasons for stating that it is at the same time both a wave and a particle, and neither one nor the other. It is neither, since a particle and a wave as objects of observation belong to the symbolic order and do not constitute the reality of the quantum system; it is both a wave and a particle, however, since "wave" and "particle" describe aspects of the mathematical formalism within which, in some way, the constitution of the quantum system is defined.

Conclusion

To summarize briefly the content of this section: it is our view that classical and quantum physics share the same operational and observable concepts, but that they differ in explanatory concepts. We shall return to this point in a later chapter.

We have also deduced that observable physical data have a two-fold reality: the *physical reality* of an observable symbol (e.g., a pointer reading, etc.), and the *intentional reality* of a property symbolised. The direct empirical object of the act of observation is the sensible symbol; the indirect object (known only through interpretation) is the property symbolised. The mathematical expression of a scientific theory parallels this twofold reality by using *mathematical symbols* in two ways, (a) to define the properties by implicit definition, and (b) to interpret the mathematical symbol observationally, i.e., by indicating what observable symbols (for example, the reading of a dial or the average of such readings), the mathematical symbol stands for.

The failure to distinguish between *observable symbol* and *physical property* can lead to a variety of philosophical opinions about the representative value of science. All forms of parallelism, for instance, lead to the fallacious view that the aim of scientific method is to construct, if possible, a perceptible (*anschaulich*) model of reality directly "translatable" into ontological terms. By "perceptible model" we mean in general, one constructed on the basis of sensible thing-to-us relations. Such a model may be thought of as a *true model* expressing reality-as-it-is-in-itself (realism), or merely as a *surrogate model* useful merely for prediction and practical purposes (instrumentalism).

With regard tó the ontological value of physics, physicists, roughly speaking, take up one of two positions. The first is a *rationalist realism* for macrophysics following the tradition of classical physics. This is often accompanied by a rationalist instrumentalism in the field of quantum physics, because of the failure of quantum physics to construct a precise model based upon the classical limiting concepts of particle and field. This is the position, for example, of Einstein, Schrödinger, Bohm, Vigier, Rosen, *et al*. It is especially characteristic of physicists who have specialised in the theory of relativity and are looking for a unitary field theoretic description of the universe. What characterises this group is a Platonic tendency to equate the meaning of *reality* with whatever can be understood conceptually, leaving empirical experience merely to provide the occasion for the recognition of existence. The second is an *empiricist realism* with regard to macrophenomena. This conceives physical reality to be no more then what is given factually in experience. This is often accompanied by an *empiricist* or *positivistic instrumentalism* in quantum physics, because the abstract norms of quantum physics, as, for example, the Psi-function, are so *unanschaulich* or unimaginable [1]. We shall return to these distinctions in a later chapter.

SECTION II: PROPOSITION (2) ON SCIENTIFIC METHOD

Proposition (2)

The act of measurement perturbs the object. Its objective state ("objective", that is, "not affected by the subjectivity of purely private

[1] See *infra*, chapter VII. For the remarks of an eminent physicist on the different philo-

experience") then cannot be known – whether as an object of empirical science (a phenomenal object) or as a reality (an object in the strict or formal sense) [1]. The Indeterminacy Principle expresses the degree of this perturbation, and thereby traces the limits of our power of knowing the physical object. Heisenberg has written: "Our ordinary description of nature, and the idea of exact laws, rests on the assumption that it is possible to observe the phenomena without appreciably influencing them. To co-ordinate a definite cause to a definite effect has sense only when both can be observed without introducing a foreign element disturbing their interrelation. The law of causality, because of its very nature, can only be defined for isolated systems, and in atomic physics even approximately isolated systems cannot be observed... for in atomic physics we are dealing with entities that are (so far as we know) ultimate and indivisible. There exist no infinitesimals by the aid of which an observation might be made without appreciable perturbation" [2]. On the Indeterminacy Principle, he says that it "refers to the degree of indeterminateness in the possible present knowledge of the simultaneous values of various quantities with which the quantum theory deals" [3].

General Criticism

The perturbation theory of measurement implies that the activities which take place between object and instrument in the measuring process serve no other function than to render some physical system or some property of it accessible to a human observer by magnifying it, otherwise "translating" it into a form in which it can produce a perceptible impression on a human observer. The measuring process is accused of perturbing to a greater or lesser extent the real physical property which one wishes to measure. This theory implies that the real physical property is *other than* what is defined by the measuring process itself. It also implies that a physical property is a thing-to-us relation. Two opinions are worth noting: (a) that of Einstein, Podolsky and Rosen who would define a physical property as what is left after the disturbance is removed [4], and (b) that of Bohr, Heisenberg and others who would say that the disturbance is not removable either in

sophical outlooks of relativists and quantum theorists, see E. Wigner, "Relativistic Invariance and Quantum Phenomena", *Rev. Mod. Phys.*, XXIX (1959), pp. 255–268.

  [1] The objectivity here denied is "public objectivity", a type of objectivity which has always been regarded as a characteristic property of scientific knowledge. Cf. chapter v.
  [2] Heisenberg, *Physical Principles* etc., pp. 62–63.
  [3] *Ibid.*, p. 20.
  [4] *Phys. Rev.*, XLVII (1935), p. 777.

fact or in principle, thus implying that all that can be known is an interaction in which subject and object are inextricably mixed. This latter position (b) leads to a distinction between *physical states* and *physical properties:* a physical state being a set of relations to possible observers which do not, however, define the physical properties of the system while a physical property is the inaccessible residue of what would be left if the disturbance could be removed. We believe that the rational outcome of this dialectic is to affirm that a property of a physical system is defined by its relations to other systems within the measuring process, and *not* with respect to the possible direct perceptible experience of a human observer. We put forward, then, a *relational theory of physical properties* [1].

The Relational Structure of Physical Properties

It is our view that a physical property (or a property of a physical system) is the term of a relation set up between the physical system and a measuring instrument: a relation resulting from the production of a formal or proper effect in the measuring instrument by the interaction during the measuring process. This proper or formal effect may not itself be a sensible datum. It may be, for example, the emission of a single photon and this is below the threshold of sensitivity. The proper effect, however, must be such that it can be subsequently transformed into a sensible datum through magnification techniques, like the use of micro-ammeters, scintillation counters, etc. It is the outcome of such a transformation that we termed an *observable symbol.*

The action between the object and the instrument is an *interaction.* There is, consequently, an effect produced in each of the interacting terms. The theory allows each of these effects to be used to measure the same property in the other member of the interacting pair. For example, the recording of a photon of energy E may be witness of an exothermic radioactive disintegration of Q-value equal to E, or, conversely, the recording of the energy of the disintegration fragments could be used as witness that a photon of energy E was emitted. Every

---

[1] Similar ideas have been put forward by P. K. Feyerabend in "Problems of Microphysics", *Frontiers of Science and Philosophy*, ed. by R. G. Colodny (London, Allen and Unwin, 1963), pp. 189–283, and by M. Sachs in "A New Approach to the Theory of Fundamental Processes", *Brit. Jour. Phil. Sci.*, xv (1964), pp. 213–243. Sachs formulates the principle that the laws of Nature must be described in terms of field variables that may be associated *only with elementary interactions* (p. 221 our italics). Weyl seems to hold a similar position, as for example, in *Gruppentheorie und Quantenmechanik*, p. 66, but the passage is not reproduced in the English translation. It is clear, however, from Appendix C of his *Philosophy of Mathematics and Natural Science*, pp. 253–265, that he too adheres essentially to the perturbation theory of measurement, though he may not have been aware of all its logical consequences.

well-designed measuring-process, then, has a structure which can be represented by the formula, $a\overleftrightarrow{P}b$, where $\overleftrightarrow{P}$ represents the interaction characteristic of the property P, and a and b are the terms affected and so correlated by the interaction. It follows then that P founds a twofold relation: (1) $a\overrightarrow{P}b$, which reads: "The formal effect of $\overrightarrow{P}$ on the instrument b, enters into the definition and measurement of the property P of the object a". (2) $a\overleftarrow{P}b$, which reads: "The formal effect of $\overleftrightarrow{P}$ on the instrument a enters into the definition and measurement of the property P of the object b".

Not every interaction between a and b is or could become a measuring-process. A necessary condition is that such an interaction should be *simple*, i.e., that a virtually single formal effect should be produced in a and in b (or if the formal effects be multiple, that all but one could be filtered out). How is one to know which interactions are potential measuring-processes and which are not? This is known not by empirical generalisation from many cases, but by interpreting the experimental process with the aid of a physical theory. It is on the authority of a physical theory (or hypothesis) that such and such an interaction is declared (positively or hypothetically) to be simple.

Each of the relations $a\overrightarrow{P}b$ and $a\overleftarrow{P}b$ is founded upon an *absolute ground* in a and in b respectively. So far as our knowledge goes, the physical property is the *absolute ground which orients the physical system to the production of an appropriate formal effect in other things*. We call the absolute ground the *primary relativity* of a physical property. What then is the absolute ground?

We have already mentioned that a definition defines not a concrete essence in its particularity, but an *ideal norm*, and an ideal norm expresses a certain similarity in which many things (actually or potentially) share. The similarity in question here is a similarity in the way things act upon one another as, for example, in the two relations $a\overrightarrow{P}b$ an $a\overleftarrow{P}b$. The property, as so defined, is an *explanatory property*. It follows from this that we only know the properties of things within a pattern of relations which is itself grounded upon a pattern of interactions. It might be surmised that another kind of intellect would be capable of knowing the ground of a property absolutely. Some might say even that the human intellect in other non-scientific kinds of knowledge would be able to know the ground of a property absolutely. However, even if this were so, it might still be doubted whether the absolute ground for any of the relations we are talking about would turn out to be intelligible apart from a World of actually related and interacting things which would give meaning to the ground. It is our view that the essential nature of the ground is to be oriented towards action with and upon things and so to the constitution of a World.

The pattern of relations which define the explanatory concepts is the physical theory. Let the relations which found the physical properties be symbolised by P_i ($i = 1, 2, \ldots,$ n); let $\overleftrightarrow{P_i}$ ($i = 1, 2, \ldots,$ n) be the corresponding interactions, and let p_i ($i = 1, 2, \ldots,$ n) be a numerical variable obtained by mapping the formal effects onto the real number field by a system of meters, circuits, etc. The mapping may be done in either of two ways: either by a direct mapping of individual concrete experiments onto the number field – this is the way of quantum mechanics; or by an indirect mapping whereby individual concrete values are taken as samples of some abstract ideal value (for example, an average value) – this is the way of classical physics [1]. Whatever manner of mapping is used, the physical theory asserts a certain set of equations:

$$f_j(p_i) = 0, \qquad j = 1, 2, \ldots, m$$

These equations have the effect of defining p_i in a mutual fashion by implicit definition of the set of variables p_i; in other words, we say that the set p_i is a self-defining set of numerical variables. As the p_i are uniquely determined with respect to the formal effects of $\overleftrightarrow{P_i}$ (through the magnification or other transformation which produces the respective observable symbol), the implicit definition of the p_i can be interpreted to mean that the set $\{\overleftrightarrow{P_i}\}$ of the physical interactivities is a self-correlated set; or, in other words, that the set of relations $\{P_i\}$ is a closed self-defining set of relations.

In quantum mechanics, the properties are represented by linear operators P_i and not by numerical variables. The equations of the axiomatic theory are operator equations on a Hilbert space of physical states. Each operator P_i represents a physical activity $\overleftrightarrow{P_i}$, and its eigen values are the possible range of values p_i. As in the former case, the operator equations have the effect of mutually defining P_i by implicit definition of the set $\{P_i\}$. This implicit definition of P_i can

---

[1] See below p. 112.

be interpreted to mean that the set $\overleftrightarrow{\{P_i\}}$ of physical activities is a self-correlated set and that the set of relations $\{P_i\}$ is a self-defining set. A pair of non-commuting operators would mean that the physical activities corresponding to these operators interfere with one another in the concrete. We shall postpone further discussion of the various interpretations of the quantum mechanical formalism to another section. For the present, it is sufficient if we have made it clear what we mean when we say that a physical property is the term of a *relation founded upon interactivity;* that its *primary relativity* is defined implicitly by an *explanatory definition* which involves a systematic totality constituted by a *mutually-defining set of interrelated properties* [1].

Returning to the act of measurement: this is completed by an *act of observation* in which the observer-scientist recognises certain sensible data either as the formal effect of a certain property P_i of the measured object, or as something uniquely derived from it through ancillary devices, such as meters, circuits, etc. Besides providing instances of a physical property P_i, the sensible data also provide the values of the secondary determinations associated with the measured property. These are the *measure-numbers* p_i of the property.

In classical physics, these measure-numbers are treated in either of two ways. (1) *Abstractly* – as samples of an idealised model of a physical process; this treatment leads to a deterministic theory like Newtonian mechanics. Consequently, the properties of classical physics are affected by a certain ideal and abstract character which is intrinsic to the method used. Or (2), they may be used as a *set of individual values,* in which case they constitute a statistical distribution (of the type of a "distribution of errors") of which the ideal classical model is the mean. A characteristic of classical physics is that a statistical theory is distinct from the deterministic theories which define the elements of the statistical ensemble.

Quantum mechanics differs from both of the older types of physical theories. It has in common with both, however, the common structure of human scientific knowing. Quantum mechanics, then, expresses both

---

[1] "The concepts with which natural science deals are not qualities or attributes which can be obtained from the objective world by direct cognition. They can only be obtained by an indirect methodology, by observing their reactions with other bodies, and their implicit definition is consequently conditioned by definite laws of nature governing reactions", H. Weyl, *Theory of Groups and Quantum Theory*, trans. by H. P. Robertson (New York: 1931), p. 76; cf. also his *Philosophy of Math.* etc., pp. 137–164. For Weyl, however, the concept does not express what is intrinsic to the physical object. For an example of how a physical theory like Newtonian Mechanics is composed of undefined elements defined implicitly by mathematical operations, cf., P. Suppes, *Introduction to Logic* (Princeton: 1957), pp. 291–304.

an *idealised model* and, at the same time, tries to make allowance for the *variety of concrete cases*. This makes the problem of separation *method* and *object* in quantum mechanics more difficult than in the older theories, since it seems to have two objects and two methods which, according to the majority of physicists, are inseparable from one another. On the other hand, quantum mechanics has a kind of simplicity which neither of the older physical theories possesses; it is concerned with the *concrete instances of the ideal model or norm* (or, alternatively, the ideal law in its concrete instances) in their simultaneous and actual union. Quantum mechanics is concerned, as Heisenberg has said, with *observation-events*, that is with physical reality in the most immediate and actual form in which it presents itself to an investigator.

A characteristic feature of a classical theory is that the six state variables of each particle, i.e., the three of position and the three of momentum, are at each instant, *independent degrees of freedom* each with a *determinate value*. Quantum physics overthrows this assumption. It shows that the measure-numbers for the six state variables are not independent *in the concrete*, and, consequently, that position and momentum do not constitute for the individual concrete particle six independent degrees of freedom.

Remnants of Classical Rationalism

Why should this discovery have shocked physicists so much? The reason was that, when quantum mechanics was discovered, physicists had long been accustomed to accept uncritically the *rationalist* outlook on physical reality characteristic of classical physics. If physical reality is the subject of a classical description, then physical reality is something ideal and abstract, viz., the content of a conceptual definition. Quantum mechanics showed that concrete reality, as manifested in empirical data, is capable of no such definition. Position and momentum are *concretely* correlated variables and not independent (aspects of a perfect conceptual model). Either physical reality was parallel to a perfect conceptual model but was unknowable, or else physical reality was known only in the concrete data. The first impact of quantum mechanics was to send science back to individual concrete experience. Science must return to the concrete, i.e., to the instances of physical reality revealed in observation events. Many elements of rationalism remained, however, in the revised outlook, of which the perturbation theory of measurement is a good example. In spite of the conversion to a basic ontological empiricism, as to what gives meaning to physical reality, the classical notion of a perfect set of measure-numbers tended to remain as the criterion which the physical reality must satisfy. The perturbation theory of measurement witnesses to the continuation of a strong current of rationalism within Heisenberg's view of complementarity. This will be discussed in chapter VIII.

We hold, on the contrary, that the perturbation which takes place when two conjugate properties are measured is a new revelation of the properties of nature, and that this has led to a more accurate definition of them, which now includes this perturbation as an *essential part*. Thus, the Indeterminacy Relations supply not less, but more, information about the object of physics then was possible before, since, in addition to describing the kinds of similarities that exist between things, it also tells us how intimately some are related to others *in concrete individual cases*.

The Indeterminacy Relation

In our interpretation of the Indeterminacy Relation (or Inde-terminacy Principle) we agree with Heisenberg in the following points: (a) that it expresses the fact that concrete acts of measuring conjugate variables generally and regularly interfere with one another [1]; (b) that it is in some way a measure of this mutual interference, and (c) that it can be interpreted in two ways: as applicable to individual systems or as applicable to ensembles of identical systems.

The Indeterminacy Principle for individual systems is expressed by the non-commutation of conjugate operators [2]; for example, of x (position) and p (the conjugate momentum). An operator represents a property of an individual system. A property, as we have said, is related to the act of measurement. Hence, the Indeterminacy Principle states something about the incompatibility of conjugate properties of an individual system *even before an actual measurement is made* [3].

The Indeterminacy Principle for ensembles of identical systems is expressed as the lower limit of the product of two standard deviations, e.g., $\overline{Dx}.\overline{Dp} \geqq h$ [4]. In this form, it is a statistical principle, and belongs properly only to ensembles of identical systems considered with respect to the *possible outcome of measurements made on each*.

[1] Heisenberg, *Physical Principles* etc., p. 3 and *passim*.
[2] *Ibid.*, pp. 118–123.
[3] *Ibid.*, pp. 13–14, 20–33.
[4] *Ibid.*, pp. 15–19, 34–46.

However, this does not exhaust the problem, for we can inquire further whether, and in what sense, the Indeterminacy Principle states that the "use of the words 'position' and 'velocity' with an accuracy exceeding that given [by this principle] is just as meaningless as the use of words whose sense is not defined" [1]. Heisenberg's answer is that, since p and x are conditioned by their respective measuring-processes, a non-compatibility of conjugate measuring processes leaves the simultaneous pair (p, x) *unrealisable* [2]; that is to say, it is *without denotation*. As Heisenberg sometimes uses *meaningless* in just this sense, we might inquire further if he thought that the simultaneous pair (p, x) was also without connotation. A logical adherence to the perturbation theory of measurement should lead to a rejection of the stronger statement. Heisenberg's intention is ambiguous; he seems, as in the passage we have just quoted, to deny even a connotation to a pair of simultaneous values (p, x); but, in other places, he clearly implies that this is not so; for example, with reference to extrapolation into the past, he is ready to concede that it might be possible to calculate exact simultaneous values for past events [3].

It is our view, however, that since the variables are also *defined* by reference to the measuring-process, the *connotation is also lacking*. However, a connotation can be lacking in one of two ways: either it is *contradictory* (i.e., nonsense), or it is *indeterminate*. For example, the actual values which specify the initial conditions of a classical system are indeterminate but not contradictory. An indeterminate case represents whatever is singular, unsystematic and irregular in a set of similar instances. Every law states only what is regularly and generally true. The statement that no deviation from the law occurs even in singular instances and unsystematically is a new law and not a corollary of the first. A minority of physicists, for example, among whom are Einstein, Popper, Bopp and Bohm [4], have held that the simultaneous pair (p, x) are determinate even if not always determinable. Margenau would hold that they are also determinable, although it would seem that an indefinite time-interval might be required for the simultaneous

[1] *Ibid.*, p. 15.

[2] *Ibid.*, pp. 20–46 where many examples of the Indeterminacy Relations are analysed.

[3] *Ibid.*, p. 20.

[4] *Albert Einstein: Philosopher-Scientist*, pp. 81–87 where Einstein summarises his view of the quantum theory, as well as the account by Bohr of his discussion with Einstein on the foundations of quantum mechanics, *ibid.*, pp. 199–242. Karl Popper, *Logic of Scientific Discovery* (London: 1959), chap. ix. F. Bopp. *Observation and Interpretation* (London: 1957), pp. 189–196. D. Bohm, *Causality and Chance in Modern Physics* (Princeton: 1957). Heisenberg lists some members of this school in *Niels Bohr* etc., pp. 12–29. Cf. *infra*, chap. v, Section iv.

measurement [1]. Suppes and Margenau have investigated the joint probability of non-commuting operators [2]. Suppes has shown that in some cases at least, as, for example, in the first excited state of the harmonic oscillator, no joint probability distribution for p and x exists, while in other cases it does. Margenau has shown that in some cases negative probability values arise. Where no joint probability distribution exists, no formula exists to give sense to a simultaneous pair of values (p, x); i.e., it is non-sense and to this degree contradictory. However, where a joint probability exists, there is no contradiction in the formula (p, x), even though the association of values has no determinate significance but only the indeterminate significance of a chance association governed by a joint probability distribution.

Having listed the three points on which we agree with Heisenberg's interpretation of the Indeterminacy Relations, we now go on to mention the three points on which we find ourselves in disagreement. We disagree with the view (1) that the Indeterminacy Relations express a *limitation* of our knowledge of physical reality; (2) that a physical property is something *other than* what is defined in and through the measuring process itself, and (3) that there is no place for an objective (i.e., publicly objective) science of microphysical objects, except as a science of *how we know* and not of *what we know*. Since this last point is based upon an analysis of the measuring process in quantum mechanics, we shall devote the next section to a detailed discussion of this.

SECTION III: THE QUANTUM THEORY OF MEASUREMENT

Three Stages of a Measurement

The quantum theory of measurement as explained by Heisenberg describes the process in three stages: (a) before the interaction of instrument and object, (b) after the interaction, and, finally, (c) the act of observation. We shall consider each of these in turn.

(a) The isolated object before the measurement is said to be a *pure case* [3], and the state is represented by a ray in abstract Hilbert space

[1] H. Margenau, *The Nature of Physical Reality* (New York: 1950), p. 376.

[2] P. Suppes, "Probability Concepts in Quantum Mechanics", *Phil. Sci.*, xxviii (1961), pp. 378–389; H. Margenau, "Measurements and Quantum States", *Phil. Sci.*, xxx (1963), pp. 138–157.

[3] A *pure case* (*reiner Fall*) or a *pure state* is one representable by a ray in Hilbert space; statistically it means that it is impossible to produce it by combining statistical ensembles with different characteristics. The term was introduced by H. Weyl and used by Heisenberg and von Neumann. Cf., H. Weyl, *Theory of Groups* etc., p. 75; J. von Neumann, *Mathematical*

which is usually taken to be a wave function $\Psi(x)$. The wave function is essentially related to a set of possible measuring processes or, as Heisenberg expresses it, it represents a *potentiality* which is actuated by a measuring process [1]. It is a *pure case*, and as such it denotes an individual something with properties some of which are precise and have definite numerical values, like rest mass, electric charge, etc., and others are imprecise but potentially precise since a precise value depends on the choice and subsequent performance of some measuring process. These potential properties occur in conjugate pairs. They are potential since exact values cannot be simultaneously assigned to both members of a pair of conjugate variables and, in the general case, no precise value need be assignable to either member of the pair. They are potential also with respect to the mathematical formalism, since value is obtained only by the mathematical transformation of the original pure case in which many values are potential into a new pure case which is the eigen state of one precise value.

The permanent precise properties of a system, like rest mass, electric charge, etc., are usually treated as invariance properties of the mathematical representation under some group of transformations. The potential properties are related to the mathematical elements of the transformation group [2]. The wave function, then, represents something of general validity in itself and is – according to Heisenberg – *objective;* but since it does not represent a body or even a coherent set of events in space and time it is *not fully objective.* "Was wir mathematisch festlegen ist nur zum kleinen Teil 'objektives Faktum', zum grösseren Teil eine Uebersicht über Möglichkeiten", said Heisenberg [3].

Since a pure case is mathematically well-defined, it represents an ideal, abstract norm, which is a concept. This concept, moreover, has reference to a concrete individual system, since experimental evidence has shown that variables like energy, momentum, etc., are conserved in collisions between individual systems. The quantum description, in spite of the fact that it yields only statistical laws, intends to be a description of an individual system and not merely of

---

Foundations etc., pp. 306–307, 328–329; Heisenberg, *Physical Principles* etc., p. 56. The difference between a pure case and a mixture has been studied by E. P. Wigner in "The Problem of Measurement", *Am. Jour Phys.*, xxxi (1963), p. 6, and by H. Margenau, *Phil. Sci.*, xxx (1963), pp. 138–157.

[1] W. Heisenberg, *Niels Bohr* etc., p. 27; *Physics and Philosophy*, pp. 41, 53, 91, 180, 185; *On Modern Physics* (London: 1961), p. 9.

[2] "All quantum numbers, with the exception of the so-called principal quantum number, are indices characterising representations of groups", H. Weyl, *Theory of Groups* etc. p. xxi.

[3] Heisenberg, *Dialectica, loc. cit.*, p. 333.

the properties of a collective. The pure case (or wave function), moreover, connotes a whole form, since the wave function which represents it, changes deterministically and predictably, evolving through a perfectly definite series of wave functions, governed by the appropriate Schrödinger equation. It connotes then something which is formally one, whole and complete.

On the other hand, the only predictions made by the theory are *statistical*, and, consequently, the pure case is in some sense incomplete and imprecise. The pure case also describes a statistical ensemble of concrete cases, each characterised by the same wave function. There is a parallel between the "pure case" in quantum mechanics and the "state" of a classical system. The theoretical representation of an individual system in classical physics is (as we have already noted) an *idealised and abstract norm,* of which actual concrete systems constitute a random sample. Classical physics deals with this ensemble by getting help from outside, viz., from a statistical "theory of errors"; quantum mechanics on the other hand includes the statistical analysis within its own formalism. This, as we have already pointed out, is connected with the human way of scientific knowing.

Returning to the quantum theory of measurement: we are at a loss to know how to treat Heisenberg's view of the nature of the measuring process since he is not the author of the "standard" or "orthodox" view. However, it is generally held that "the standard view is an outgrowth of Heisenberg's paper in which the uncertainty relation was first formulated" [1]; and it is clear from the brief defence Heisenberg made of it in 1955 that the regards it as the only authentic account [2]. The first to explore the consequences of Heisenberg's ideas and to base a theory of measurement on them was von Neumann who published his classic work on the mathematical foundations of quantum mechanics in 1932 [3]. His view has come to be called the "orthodox" view of the Copenhagen School. The clearest summary of it, and the account from which we shall quote, is that given by London and Bauer [4].

Let the wave function before the measurement be denoted by $\Psi'(x)$, and let $\Psi_k(x)$, $k = 1, 2, \ldots$, be a complete set of eigen functions of

[1] E. P. Wigner, *Am. Jour. Phys.*, XXXI (1963), p. 6.
[2] Heisenberg, *Niels Bohr* etc., p. 27.
[3] J. von Neumann, *Mathematische Grundlagen* usw., translated under the title *Mathematical Foundations of Quantum Mechanics*.
[4] F. London and E. Bauer, *La théorie de l'observation en mécanique quantique* (Paris: Hermann, 1939).

(say) the momentum P, where the corresponding eigen values of P are p_k, $k = 1, 2, \ldots$. Then $\Psi(x)$ can be written in the following way:

$$\Psi(x) = \Sigma_k \, a_k \Psi_k(x)$$

where

$$\Sigma_k \, |a_k|^2 = 1$$

This is a pure case.

The process of measurement itself takes place in two stages: (b) the interaction between the object and the apparatus which is represented mathematically by the transformation of the pure case Ψ into a *mixture* of the states $\Psi_k(x)$, and (c) an act of observation which "registers" which of the states $\Psi_k(x)$ has been "actualised" by the interaction.

Formation of a Mixture

Let us consider first of all the interactions between the object and the apparatus; and let the property measured by the apparatus be the momentum P. The object-plus-apparatus comprises a closed and isolated macroscopic physical system which is subject to the laws of physics. Assuming that the quantum theory applies also to macroscopic systems, it will have a comprehensive wave function χ in which both the variables of the object, viz., x, p, etc., and the variables of the apparatus, viz., y, q, etc., will be present. Let the variable which is correlated with the measured property P of the object be z. Let z_0, $z_1, \ldots z_i, \ldots$ be its eigen values (they are, say, the positions of a pointer on a scale) and let $\Phi_0(y)$, $\Phi_1(y)$, $\ldots \Phi_i(y)$, $\ldots$ be the corresponding eigen functions of the apparatus. Then, the nature of a measuring apparatus is that there should exist such a correspondence between the states $\Psi_k(x)$ of the object and the states $\Phi_k(y)$ of the apparatus, that from the pointer reading z_k of the apparatus, the value p_k for the momentum of the object can be inferred.

Before the interaction, the comprehensive wave function χ was simply the product of the wave function Ψ of the object and of the wave function Φ_0 of the zero state of the apparatus: i.e.,

$$\chi = \Psi \, \Phi_0 = \Sigma_k \, a_k \Psi_k \, \Phi_0$$

After the interaction, the only form which the comprehensive wave function $\chi(\text{final}) = \chi_f$ can have, and which is in keeping with the nature and function of the measuring-process is,

$$\chi_f = \Sigma_k \, a_k \Psi_k \Phi_k$$

That is, to every Ψ'_k there is coupled a Φ_k, or in other words, from every potential value z_k of the apparatus, we can infer a corresponding value p_k for the momentum of the object. The final state χ_f of the combined instrument and object is a pure case as long as they constitute an isolated system and, as long as this is true, the values z_k are only potential in the wave function, for it represents the total system.

A measurement, however, does not consider the total combined system, but only one part of it, viz., the apparatus. Examining the total wave function χ_f for the information it can yield about the state of the apparatus, it can be shown that this is represented by what is called a *mixture* of the eigen states Φ_k present in χ_f. Another *mixture*, but this time of the Ψ'_k is in one-to-one correspondence with this and represents the condition of the object. A *mixture* is a virtual ensemble of different pure cases, each present with a certain determinate probability; here the probability associated with Φ_k and with Ψ'_k is $|a_k|^2$. That is, from the point of view of the apparatus, the original pure case Ψ of the object is transformed into a *mixture* containing all the eigen states present in Ψ, each with its determinate probability now *actuated* by the interaction. Such a mixture is an ordinary Gibb's ensemble like those used in classical statistical mechanics [1]. The state of the system is now determinate but still unknown. The situation might be compared with a card drawn at random from a pack of cards, in which each card is marked with one of the Ψ'_k and each Ψ'_k is represented in the pack with a frequency proportional to $|a_k|^2$. The ideal frequency of a set of random drawings from the pack is predicted by the theory, but what the result will be in any concrete case cannot be inferred from it. At this stage of the measurement, the quantum mechanical situation would be like a card drawn from such a pack, lying face down and not yet scrutinized. The quantum mechanical case has by now been transformed into a case of classical statistics.

Act of Observation

The measurement is completed by an act of observation which ascertains which of the pointer values z_k has been actuated by the interaction. From a pointer value z_k, one concludes that the object,

---

[1] The reduction of a pure case to a mixture is often described as a *projection* of the pure case on to its eigenstates; for the pure case is represented by a ray in Hilbert space which is spanned by a complete set of eigenstates as if each of these were a coordinate axis in the Hilbert space. The reduction of a pure case to a mixture is its projection on to the "coordinate axes" of the space; the probability that a projection will take place along any particular axis is proportional to the squared length of its projection on this axis. For this reason, the measuring process is often called a *projection operator*.

immediately after the measurement, is in the pure state Ψ'_k. Thus, the final act of observation is a process of sampling the mixture (which is a probability distribution) and of registering the contingent factual outcome.

One fact, however, should be noted; that the comprehensive wave function χ_f for the combined object-apparatus system considered in isolation from its surrounding contains more information than do the separate mixtures produced by the interaction. Certain correlations between the states of the object and those of the apparatus – viz., superposition states – have been destroyed by the measurement [1]. This results in an increase in entropy of the entire system consequent upon the act of observation [2].

Apart from its more subtle and complicated character, which distinguishes it from the theory of measurement in classical physics, the quantum mechanical theory of measurement seems to be straightforward enough and obscure philosophical questions seem to be fairly remote. However, just as the initial insight of Heisenberg into the foundations of physics was fraught with philosophical consequences, so the defects in his philosophical view came to be incorporated into the very heart of quantum mechanics, viz., into the theory of measurement.

The Observer in Quantum Mechanics

According to Heisenberg, the function of the observer is to "register decisions" [3], i.e., to record which of the possibilities contained in the statistical mixture described above has in fact been actualised by the measurement. He says that the recording can be done as well by a photographic-plate as by a human observer. However, as Wigner and others have shown, this does not follow from the theory, since in so far as the object-plus-instrument-plus-photographic-plate constitute a larger isolated system, the theory allows one to deduce no more than the pure case. To obtain verifiable formulae, one must pass to the next stage, namely, of the formation of a mixture, and this supposes that the system is subject to a super act of observation from outside which interferes with the state of the system. To go from the pure state to

---

[1] "Of paramount philosophical significance... is that (3) the whole is always more, is capable of a much greater variety of wave states than the combination of the parts. Disjoint parts in an isolated system of fixed wave states are in general not statistically independent even if they do not interact", H. Weyl, *Philosophy of Math.* etc., p. 263; cf. also, London and Bauer, *loc. cit.*, pp. 34–37.

[2] London and Bauer, *loc. cit.*, p. 30; also von Neumann, *loc. cit.*, pp. 379–398. Cf. also Appendix, pp. 180–2.

[3] Heisenberg, *Niels Bohr* etc., p. 22.

the mixture, and thence to the question of fact, a union must take place between the photographic-plate and the sensibility of a human observer. While this union is *physically* no different from that between object and apparatus, the human sensibility, however, has the "characteristic and familiar power which we can call the 'power of introspection'" [1] by which it can take cognizance of its own state, and so emerge from the indeterminacy of a mixture to the determinacy of fact by an act of auto-observation [2]. From a knowledge of his own state, the human observer infers the correlative state in which the object finds itself after the measurement. The process of passing from the initial pure state of the object to the final pure state after observation is called the "reduction of the wave packet". It is physical as we have already explained; it is psychological since it requires the intervention of a human act of auto-observation, and it is also logical because, in the language of complementarity, the wave picture dissolves into that of the complementary particle picture, and this fact gives its name to the entire process, viz., the "reduction" or "contraction of the wave packet".

Reduction of the Wave Packet

One of the most controversial topics in quantum mechanics to-day is the *reduction of the wave packet*. There are three problems. (1) Does the *reduction* entail a real occurrence in the physical object independent of the conscious act of observation; or is it merely a "reduction of knowledge", i.e., a change in representation due to the acquisition of new information about the object without entailing a significant change in the object; or does it include both of these? This will be discussed in the next chapter. (2) Is the *Projection Postulate* a necessary part of quantum mechanics? That is: is a definite eigen state the new pure state produced by the act of measurement or does the act of measurement measure the state as it was *before* the measurement, whatever happens to the system after or as a result of the measurement (e.g., the system might be destroyed by the measurement as, for example, when a photon is absorbed)? This is principally a physical

---

[1] London and Bauer, *loc. cit.*, p. 42.

[2] Note how the act of auto-observation, as described by London and Bauer, assumes a coincidence or at least a parallelism between consciousness (i.e., the content of the conscious act of observation) and the physical substratum (i.e., the physical state of the eyes, nerves, brain, etc., of the human observer). Implied in this account is also the theory that consciousness (or rather acts of observation of reality) also follows quantum mechanical laws. We shall return to this later in chap. v.

problem and it will not be discussed in this book [1]. (3) Is the "reduction of the wave packet" a process essentially different from the mere sampling of a statistical distribution, whether this be a classical (stochastic) distribution or one of some non-classical type? This problem will be discussed in the section entitled "Formal Objectivity" in the next chapter and in chapter VI.

Heisenberg, von Neumann, Wigner, London and Bauer regard the reduction of the wave packet as a new and unique kind of psychophysical *projection operator* terminating in the projection on to the plane of actuality of one of the potential states represented in the wave packet. Many physicists find this explanation unclear and permeated with dubious epistemological presuppositions. Landé complains: "No agreement has been reached whether the said 'contraction' is physical, mental, real, pictorial, objective or subjective. But something must contract, since Heisenberg said so thirty years ago" [2].

Objectivity of Quantum Mechanics

A disturbing question is suggested by the views of Heisenberg, Wigner, von Neumann and others, that the (private) sensibility of the individual human observer is an essential determinant of the object of quantum mechanics. If this is so, how can public objectivity, a necessary condition of all science, exist in quantum mechanics?

One answer is that given by London and Bauer [3]. The instrument and the eye are macroscopic systems. Hence, the quantum mechanical treatment of the link between the two must approach the classical limit, which is, of course, the paragon of public objectivity. They argue that the coupling between the eye and the apparatus changes the apparatus only negligibly and that, consequently, the same correspondence exists between the apparatus and the eye of any observer [4].

---

[1] Among those physicists who reject the *Projection Postulate* are, Margenau, Landé, Feyerabend, Schrödinger. Cf. H. Margenau, *Phil. Sci.*, xxx (1963), 1–16, 138–157; P. K. Feyerabend, *Frontiers of Science and Philosophy*; A. Landé, *From Dualism to Unity in Quantum Mechanics* (Cambridge: 1960); E. Schrödinger, *Naturwiss.*, xxiii (1935), p. 812.

[2] A. Landé, "From Dualism to Unity in Quantum Mechanics", in *Current Issues in the Philosophy of Science*, ed. by H. Feigl and G. Maxwell (New York: 1961), p. 355.

[3] London and Bauer, *loc. cit.* pp. 48–51; also D. Bohm, *Quantum Theory* (New York: Prentice-Hall, 1951); G. Ludwig, *Die Grundlagen der Quantenmechanik* (Berlin: 1954); P. K. Feyerabend, *Observation and Interpretation* (London: 1957); A. Daneri, A. Loinger, G. M. Prosperi, *Nucl. Phys.*, xxxiii (1962), p. 297.

[4] Recent studies have shown that the size of the apparatus is of considerable importance to the measurement. E. Wigner and H. Salecker showed the necessity of relatively massive apparatus for the precise determination of time (*Phys. Rev.*, cix, 1958, p. 571); for the influence of the size of the apparatus on the accuracy of measurements, cf., E. Wigner,

London and Bauer conclude their study with the reassuring statement: "The possibility of prescinding from the individuality of the observer and of creating a collective scientific consciousness cannot be seriously questioned" [1].

This answer is based upon the Correspondence Principle and upon the assumption that quantum mechanics, in so far as it is applicable to macro-phenomena, gives nothing more that what classical physics would give in these cases. This is a common view of the Correspondence Principle, and not altogether a correct one; for quantum physics could give classical results in certain appropriate limiting cases without excluding the possibility that quantum physics contains something more, for example, a more exact explanation of the relation between observer-subject and observed-object in physics – even of macroscopic phenomena. Heisenberg, Wigner, von Neumann, for example, clearly imply that something more is given [2]. Others, like Ludwig, try to avoid this conclusion by restricting the applicability of quantum physics to microscopic phenomena and to marginal cases [3]. The majority of physicists, however, among whom is Heisenberg, hold that the quantum mechanical domain includes also the domain of classical physics. There is a connection between this view and the insistence on the inescapable precence of *subjectivity* in modern physics.

Summary

The philosophy of complementarity, while successful in providing physicists with a common language with which to describe quantum phenomena, also contains a theory about scientific method and about human knowing which is open to criticism. In this chapter, we criticised the following points arising out of the philosophy of complementarity: psycho-physical parallelism; the view that quantum mechanical properties are to be defined classically; and the perturbation theory

Zeit f. Physik, cxxxi (1952) p. 101; *Amer. Jour. Phys.*, xxxi (1963), p. 6; H. Araki and M. Yanase, "Measurement of Quantum Mechanical Operators", *Phys. Rev.*, cxx (1960), pp. 622–626; M. Yanase, "Optimal Measuring Apparatus", *Phys. Rev.*, cxxiii (1961), pp. 666–668. Wigner concludes: "This raises the suspicion that the macroscopic nature of the apparatus is necessary in principle" (*Am. Jour. Phys.*, xxxi, 1963, p. 6).

[1] London and Bauer, *loc. cit.*, p. 49.

[2] E. Wigner, "Remarks on the Mind-Body Problem", in *The Scientist Speculates*, ed. by I. J. Good (London: 1962), pp. 284–301; J. von Neumann, *Mathematical Foundations* etc.; W. Heisenberg, *Niels Bohr* etc., pp. 12–29.

[3] G. Ludwig, "Gelöste und ungelöste Probleme des Messprozesses", in *Werner Heisenberg und die Physik unserer Zeit*, ed. by F. Bopp (Braunschweig: 1961), pp. 150–181. Ludwig has changed his view from that expressed in his *Grundlagen* usw.

of measurement. In the course of the criticism, we elaborated the distinction between two types of concepts with different logical structures; viz., *operational* or *observational concepts* which state a similarity between things judged on the basis of appearance or utility *to us*, and *explanatory concepts* which state a similarity between things judged on the basis of a self-defining set of different relations between things. We have shown how a physical concept is definable by any appropriate measuring-process. The description of the measuring-process and, hence, the definition of the physical property involve the two classes of concepts described above, but in different ways. This leads us to regard the Indeterminacy Relations, not as stating limitations of our knowledge, but as describing more exactly the behaviour of individual systems.

CHAPTER FIVE

SUBJECTIVITY AND OBJECTIVITY

SECTION I: SUBJECTIVITY AND OBJECTIVITY DEFINED

Public Objectivity

Objectivity, the property of being an object of human knowledge, has many senses. In the first place, it can mean the property of being valid for a general public; its contrary being the subjectivity of the private, individual and incommunicable act. This kind of objectivity, which we call *public objectivity*, is necessary for objects of natural science. There are, however, two kinds of public objectivity. One belongs to an *idea* (or concept), and the other belongs to a *reality in its World*. The former is that property possessed by an exact and precise definition, namely, of being independent of particular places, times and factual occurrences; this belongs not to any World of the real, but to the realm of ideas. The latter, however, belongs to a shared World of real things. It is the object of factual judgements, founded upon perception and – unlike the precision of an idea – it is accompanied by an irreducible element of impreciseness and indeterminateness.

Public objectivity, as Kant saw it, is based upon the presence of pure synthetic *a priori* features in our knowledge. Such features are the "axioms of intuition", the "anticipations of experience", the "analogies of experience" and the "postulates of empirical thought in general" [1]. Euclidean geometry, causality (in the sense of antecedent-consequent legality between successive phenomena), the permanence of "substance" were universal and necessary aspects of scientific thought because, for Kant, they belonged to the intentionality-structure of every scientific question. Heisenberg, on the other hand, points out again and again that relativity and quantum mechanics have shown that it is sufficient if the conditions just described be universal

---

[1] I. Kant, *Critique of Pure Reason*, trans. by Norman Kemp Smith (London, Macmillan, 1963), pp. 194–256.

only in a well-defined domain and necessary only as a matter of fact. That is, the Kantian synthetic *a priori* elements of natural science give no more than a possible and hypothetical ground for the construction of a scientific object; a process of empirical testing has to be employed to ascertain whether or not the possible and hypothetical ground is an explanation in fact in this domain and where the boundaries of its domain of applicability are to be found.

Besides the Kantian *a priori*, there are also other *a priori* elements which can ground the public objectivity of a scientific object. These are the forms of possible physical theories, mathematical structures for the most part, suggested by empirical data and originating in acts of creative enriching insight. These theories are *a priori* to experience, not in the sense that they are antecedent to all experience like Kant's Pure Science of Nature, but because they are antecedent to the process of empirical testing on the basis of which alone a theory is accepted or rejected. A theory has the structure of an ideal norm composed of a self-defining set of relations. Because the norms are ideal and do not involve acts of perception, these may be shared by a community of scientists who speak the same scientific language, and who can make independent tests of any theory irrespective of particular places and times. The theoretical entities or objects constructed by this process have a common and public value which defines a kind of objectivity which we are tempted to call scientific objectivity, but, since we envisage the problem of such entities within the broader context of being, we prefer to use the term *public objectivity*.

In the second place, let us distinguish from one another, several classes of public objects and their noumenal correlates.

Thing

The first class of public objects is an object which is a unity, identity, whole and the stable subject of properties; it may be either an object given in perception or a constructed object, like an electron, which is linked by us to reality through observable symbols. In either case, the transcendent being correlated with this object, if such exists, is called by us a *thing*. A subdivision of *thing* is *body*.

Body

The second class of public objects is a *phenomenal object*, to which corresponds a *body* (in the strict sense) as its noumenal correlate. A phenomenal object belongs to the class of objects which, as Husserl said, are "given primordially in perception". It might be described as a stable subject of perceptible properties in a spatially organised World. Allied to the notion of body as the transcendent correlate of a phenomenal – and, therefore, perceptible – object, there are two limiting concepts which we shall include under the name *body:* they are: (1) whatever is conceived to have determinate spatial coordinates at each instant – as, for example, a classical body or a classical particle – even though it might not be perceptible, and (2) a *field* which is conceived to be an infinitely extended medium for three-dimensional wave motions. These last two classes of objects enter the sphere of reality through their respective observable symbols.

Empirical Objectivity

The kind of objectivity which is based upon the exteriority of subject and object in perception is given by us the name *empirical objectivity*. This is divided into *phenomenal objectivity* for the phenomenal object) and *bodily objectivity* (for a body). This kind of object, however, is not so constituted by the act of knowing that it is entirely separated from or independent of all subjectivity; exteriority implies its correlate interiority, viz., of a subject. It is then always an object-for-me.

Formal Objectivity

While it would evidently be contradictory to state that within the relation of bodily or phenomenal objectivity a subject could simultaneously be the subject and object of knowledge; there is a kind of objectivity in which even the subject can know itself objectively: we call this *formal objectivity*. This is an objectivity constituted by an affirmation which simply releases it from dependence on a knowing subject as such. It belongs to whatever is affirmed as a virtually unconditioned object on the basis of evidence. In physics, this evidence is provided by a process of testing and verification. This kind of object we call an *object in the strict or formal sense;* for its intention is simply to express *what is,* independently of the act whereby I know it as an object-for-me. The noumenal correlate of an object in the strict or formal sense (or a strict object) is an individual existing being, or a relation between individual existing beings.

Although formal objectivity according to its definition is different from both bodily and public objectivity, it is nevertheless implied by both of these types and is in fact an essential element of both. For the bodily object which is out there, exterior to me as a bodily subject, is also – except in phenomenalist metaphysics – affirmed to have an existence independently of the relation of exteriority which it has acquired to myself as a knowing subject. The relation of exteriority to a knowing bodily subject is not constitutive of the body-in-itself, but is a relation added to some absolute ground which exists (we may not know how or by what) independently of its phenomenal presentation within the field of my perception. Even pure phenomenalism however cannot escape formal objectivity; for the very positing of phenomenalism as a true philosophy is an act whose sense is to separate a certain mental content from its dependence on my or any subjectivity. This mental content is an object to which the relation of bodily exteriority simply does not apply: it has, however, public objectivity.

Public objectivity also implies formal objectivity and contains it within itself. There are two kinds of public objectivity: of an idea and of a reality in its World. We are here concerned with ideas only in so far as they are asserted or affirmed of something given in experience and hence as a property of a real situation within a World. An idea however may state the relation of a thing to a knowing subject or a relation existing between things. In either case, the terms of the relation are presupposed by the relation and posited in some way to exist independently of their relation to my subjectivity; that is, the relation to my subjectivity is merely the means through which some absolute ground makes itself present to me in my experience. This is very evident in the case of ideas which, like physical properties, express thing-to-thing relations; for even, if it should be argued that the relation generates its own terms, neither of the terms of a thing-to-thing relation is (in physics) a knowing subject and hence the positing of such a relation satisfies the definition of formal objectivity in a special way.

These considerations however suggest an important question: Is formal objectivity to be atrributed equally to every aspect of the public object? Or are there aspects to which public objectivity can be correctly attributed but which lack nevertheless formal objectivity? Let us recall that it is sufficient for a public object merely that it be understood, recognised and described by all in the same way. Consequently, public objectivity does not require that *a priori* subjective elements, if there are any, which are common to a certain way of knowing but are nevertheless extrinsic to that which is formally and strictly affirmed, should be consciously distinguished from the content of that which is strictly affirmed. These *a priori* elements of the public object belong to the intentionality-structure of the knowing in so far as this is a human method of doing scientific research, and they constitute the matrix in which the strict object makes its appearance. The disengagement of the strict object from its setting of scientific methodology is, we believe, one of the principal epistemological problems of quantum mechanics, and we reserve this problem for section III of the present chapter.

Reality and its Criterion

Let us distinguish, moreover, the *meaning* of the term "reality" from the *criterion* of reality with reference to a certain knower. The former defines what is meant by the term. The latter is that on account of which a thing is said by a certain knower to be real: in our case, it is the sign through which its reality is manifested to us. In the rationalist intentionality-structure of classical physics, "reality" means "a body in the strict sense (but with idealised boundaries and coordinates), or whatever agrees with the limiting concepts of classical particle or classical field". Its criterion is the appearance in experience of an appropriate – if vague – indication of its presence such as, e.g., the recording of a non-vanishing field intensity. In the empiricist view, "reality" means "whatever is here and now perceived as a body in the strict sense". For it, the *meaning* and the *criterion* of reality are identified. Anticipating a later section, let us state here our own view for the sake of completeness: (1) the criterion of physical reality in regard of a human knower is not identical with its meaning, since we have no intellectual intuition of physical reality; (2) the *meaning* of "reality" is "whatever is defined by the object in the formal sense", while (3) its *criterion* is a manifestation of its presence through *observable symbols*, and critically judged to be such, within a World of real things.

Subjectivity

Just as there are many kinds of objectivity, so there are many kinds of *subjectivity*. This we define to be the *absence of a corresponding kind of objectivity*. There is then (i) a subjectivity which is an *absence of empirical objectivity*. This may be either the type of interiority which is the strict correlate of the exteriority of an empirical object, or simply a lack of bodily objectivity. The latter is one of the senses in which the quantum mechanical system is said to be non-objective. (ii) There is subjectivity which is an *absence of public objectivity*. This is the subjectivity of unshared or incommunicable private experience or observation. This too is said to be a new and inescapable factor of quantum mechanical science. Finally, (iii) there is a subjectivity which is the *absence of sufficient evidence for the virtually unconditioned affirmation of a strict object*. This is the subjectivity attached to a mere supposition or hypothesis.

SECTION II: EMPIRICAL OBJECTIVITY

Objectivity and Exteriority

Quantum mechanics denies that an atomic physical system is objectifiable as a *body;* i.e., it says that a quantum mechanical system does not possess precisely determinable space-time coordinates and momenta independently of particular acts of measurement and observation. The denial in question refers to the *public empirical objectivity* of a body. This is a direct consequence of the Principle of Complementarity. "Science", as Heisenberg said, "no longer confronts nature as an objective observer" [1]; the objects of science are not bodies, existing *out there* in isolated exteriority to the knowing subject. From this denial of the exteriority of the object, Heisenberg went to the opposite extreme and concluded that the object was really an interior act: "The object of research is no longer nature itself, but man's investigation of nature. Here... man confronts himself alone" [2].

The failure of an objectivity founded upon exteriority alone, however, does not entail as a necessary consequence the kind of interiority in which "man confronts himself alone"; for there is a third possibility, viz., a more discriminating critique of the subject-object relation in science, and a better analysis of the structure of the scientific object in the strict or formal sense [3].

A more careful analysis of the subject-object relations shows that

[1] Heisenberg, *Physicist's Conception of Nature*, p. 29.

[2] *Ibid.*, p. 24.

[3] That the principal kind of objectivity envisaged by most physicists is one based upon the relation of exteriority, is illustrated by von Neumann's account of the measuring process (*Mathematical Foundations of Quantum Mechanics*, chap. vi, especially pp. 420–421). Here he uses the principle of *psycho-physical parallelism* to establish the distinction and relation between subject and object in the measuring process; the division between the two, in his account, is evidently a spatial division, which he called the *Schnitt* or *boundary*. "That the boundary can be pushed arbitrarily deeply into the interior of the actual observer is the content of the principle of psycho-physical parallelism..., but this does not change the fact that in each method of description the boundary must be put *somewhere*" (my italics), *ibid.*, p. 420. Heisenberg paraphrases this passage in *Niels Bohr* etc., p. 27.

there are many different kinds based upon a variety of different differentiating relations. The exteriority of a body vis-à-vis a human knower as a bodily subject is not the only kind of objectivity which a scientific object can have. In fact, it would be a serious misunderstanding of scientific method to state that objectivity of this kind belongs *essentially* to a physical system as known. This was one of the errors of the intentionality-structure of classical physics.

Empirical objectivity belongs to a unity, identity whole which is *perceived as such;* a physical system, however, is a thing, i.e., a unity, identity whole which is the subject of physical properties. We have already shown that physical properties are not defined relative to perception, but relative to a self-correlated set of interactions between things. It follows from this that neither a physical property nor a physical system contains in its definition anything that relates it intrinsically to elements of perception. Comparing the definition of a *physical system* with that of a *body*, we see that the former in no way implies – though it does not exclude – that it be a body. What actually is perceived by a scientist is a complex of bodies and bodily properties which comprise the measuring apparatus. This is the context in which the observable symbol occurs, which is the criterion that manifests to us the reality of a quantum mechanical system. That the physical system should itself be one of the bodies of this complex is not required by the physical theory.

The failure of empirical objectivity for microscopic systems, then, is not only understandable, but it might well have been anticipated by a more careful analysis of scientific method. We do not mean to say that Heisenberg's Indeterminacy Relations should have been predicted on the basis of an analysis of scientific method; for this is founded upon new empirical data; but that the rearguard action in favour of theories of a "classical sort" should have been dropped long ago, and for reasons based upon the logic of scientific method.

SECTION III: PUBLIC OBJECTIVITY

Heisenberg and Public Objectivity

Public objectivity, as we have seen, is a necessary condition of science; since, without it, there could be no scientific community, no scientific language and no collaboration towards well-defined goals. It is surprising, then, that many physicists should find that the possibility of this kind of objectivity is restricted by the formal structure of quantum mechanics.

Heisenberg never doubted the public objectivity of quantum mechanics. It was for him one of the indubitable facts which were the starting point of his philosophy. "The physicist", he wrote, "must postulate in his science that he is studying a world which he himself has not made, and which would be present, essentially unchanged, if he were not there" [1]. The critical problem in the philosophy of science, as Heisenberg saw it, was to express the *a priori* conditions of possibility – both subjective and objective – of a science which, like quantum mechanics, contradicted so many of the universal and necessary conditions accepted both as a part of pure science and as a part of philosophy since the time of Kant.

The contrast between the public objectivity of quantum physics as a science and the "subjective element" in the acts which comprise the exercise of this science, is brought out in many parts of Heisenberg's writings. "The objective reality of the elementary particle has been strangely dispersed", he wrote, "not into the fog of some ill-defined or still unexplained conception of reality, but into the transparent clarity of a mathematics which no longer describes the behaviour of elementary particles, but only our knowledge of their behaviour" [2]. Again in his celebrated article contributed to the collection, *Niels Bohr and the Development of Physics* (1955), he wrote: "This representation [of a closed system by a ray in Hilbert space] ... is completely 'objective', i.e., it no longer contains features connected with the observer's knowledge, but it is also completely abstract and incomprehensible since the mathematical expressions $\Psi(q)$, $\Psi(p)$, etc., do not refer to real space or to a real property, it thus, so to speak, contains no physics at all" [3]. Such a description is "complete and objective" but "not real". To make this a "description of Nature" it has to be linked to the question of "how real or possible experiments will result". The interaction of the system with the measuring apparatus is described mathematically by a mixture and "thus the description contains, besides its objective features, ... information about the extent of the observer's knowledge of the system" [4]. This latter, he calls, the "subjective element" in our knowledge of nature; since a mixture gives only "incomplete information" about the actual state of the

[1] Heisenberg, *Niels Bohr* etc., p. 24.
[2] Heisenberg, *Physicist's Conception of Nature*, p. 15.
[3] Heisenberg, *Niels Bohr* etc., pp. 26–27.
[4] *Ibid.*

object. The "subjective element" in question belongs to the sphere of the private experience of the observer.

The "Subjective Element"

For Heisenberg, the "subjective element" in quantum mechanics is twofold: (1) the failure of empirical objectivity (in the sense of classical physics) for quantum mechanical systems, and (2) the failure of public objectivity in quantum mechanics resulting in an insurmountable subjective barrier limiting public knowledge of atomic systems to irreducibly probabilistic laws.

The failure of empirical objectivity led to a rejection of the rationalist view of reality. One would think that Heisenberg, like Bohr, swung to the other extreme, of outright empiricism. This is indeed the impression one receives – for example, from his insistence that reality is encountered only in what is actually experienced, i.e., in "observation events", and that the true description of reality is always of happenings in three-dimensional space. His original insight on the importance of *observables* in physics contained, as we have already shown, a strong empirical element. However, Heisenberg, the theoretical physicist, had a strong rationalist bias and this led him eventually to an explicit rejection of empiricism. Being persuaded of the rationality of nature, he saw in Berkeley and Locke an abdication of the power of reason [1]. We shall examine in another chapter the attempts he made to overcome this twofold crisis [2].

The outcome of this tension in Heisenberg was a synthesis of the two dialectical extremes by means of a Kantian distinction between an empirical reality represented by the phenomenal object and a noumenal reality or thing-in-itself, which would be the content of an intellectual intuition of physical reality, *if we had such an intuition*. However, Heisenberg surmises that we have no such intellectial intuition and consequently that reality in the sense of *thing-in-itself* is formally unknowable by us. Nevertheless, we are not deprived of all contact with noumenal reality, since human reason and empirical intuition preserve a symbolic vestige of it in so far as they are related by their activity to an unspecified noumenal correlate. Rationalism and empiricism are both rejected but ultimately reconciled on the deeper level of the knowing subject where they express different aspects of the dynamic structure of human intentionality. The outcome of this is to divide the

---

[1] Heisenberg, *Physics and Philosophy*, p. 83.
[2] *Infra*, chap. VIII.

meaning of "reality" into two: a *phenomenal reality* defined as the object of categorised empirical intuition, and a *noumenal reality* defined as the object of a kind of intellectual intuition which we do not possess.

Originally, for Heisenberg, these were the only *objective meanings* of reality. The quantum mechanical system, however, does not fulfil either meaning. Although every observation-event of a quantum mechanical system terminates in the empirical realities of the measuring instrument and its response, no well-defined permanent and causally-related phenomenal object can be formed of the quantum mechanical system and, consequently – assuming parallelism – no well-defined noumenal correlate exists. The failure of the quantum mechanical system to satisfy either of the two definitions of "reality", was for a long time blamed by Heisenberg on a radical insufficiency of the human knowing subject. Knowing neither the empirical nor the noumenal reality of the quantum mechanical system, the human knower was forced to represent it by an artificially constructed idea, viz., the wave function, which "contains no physics at all" [1]. In later years, Heisenberg proposed a third and new meaning for the term "reality", to which he gave the names "potentia", "objective tendency", or "objective possibility". This was neither a pure idea, nor an actual event (an empirical object), but it was a real possibility of producing *ideal frequencies* [2].

The root cause of Heisenberg's perplexity is to be found in his inadequate theory of knowledge and scientific method, and particularly in an underlying parallelism which assumes that the reality of a physical system or property is either the direct object of an act of observation (a phenomenal reality) or something directly correlated with it in a parallelistic sense (a body or the kind of bodily property which is founded upon a thing-to-us relation). If this is assumed, then, the quantum mechanical system, to which no stable and coherent empirical object corresponds, is not real in either of the two senses discussed. The direct object of an act of observation is not, however, as we have shown, the reality of the physical system. It is merely its observable symbol. The lack of coherence of a set of sensible symbols (in this case, of two mutually exclusive sets, namely, discrete or particle symbols and continuous or field symbols) does not imply a lack of coherence in the thing symbolised. Moreover, the connection between the observable symbol and reality is not one

---

[1] *Ibid.*
[2] Cf., *ibid.*, p. 13; *Physics and Philosophy*, pp. 41, 53, 70, 91 and 185.

of parallelism in the usual sense for, if this were so, reality would be as incoherent as the symbol; its relation to reality is far more complicated and will be discussed in chapter IX.

As for the irreducibly probabilistic nature of quantum mechanical laws, we have stated our view that this does not imply such an incursion of private subjectivity that our power of knowing reality suffers an essential check at the quantum level. Probabilistic laws do not spring from ignorance nor from the inescapable perturbation of an object by an observer-subject, but they arise as a necessary consequence of our abstractive mode of knowing individual and concrete things. Only an ideal norm can be defined precisely by the human mind. This always has the structure of a law from which concrete cases diverge only randomly. Random deviations lead to statistical laws. Hence, quantum mechanics, in which we find the organic union of both statistical and deterministic laws, expresses the most general form in which a scientific theory can be expressed by a human investigator. We shall return to these points later on.

Problem of Public Objectivity in Quantum Mechanics

For many physicists, however, the logic of quantum mechanics leads to the conclusion that quantum mechanics is concerned with the private act of observation of a scientific observer and that, moreover, this private act is capable of destroying previously existing correlations and so of effecting public and observable changes in the course of nature. Under these circumstances, the public objectivity of science is put in jeopardy.

To illustrate this problem, we shall use an example adapted from Heisenberg, changing the conditions a little in order to bring out the salient points better, but following the line of Heisenberg's argument [1].

In our exposition, we shall keep as close as possible to Heisenberg's language, thought and manner of interpreting the experiment. In the next sub-section, we shall analyse more fully the views expressed. Let us consider a beam of atoms all prepared in the state "m" (for example, of magnetic moment m) which is passed in succession through two inhomogeneous fields F_1 and F_2. Transitions take place during the passage through each field. The two fields are accompanied by separating fields which separate the different states into different beams so that an observation made on the relative position of the atom by an observer is equivalent to an observation of state (see figure).

[1] Heisenberg, *Physical Principles* etc., pp. 59–62.

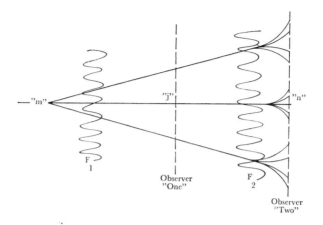

There is an observer (observer "One") placed at an intermediate position between F_1 and F_2; and a second observer (observer "Two") placed on the far side of F_2. Each observer has an apparatus designed to measure an atom's position, which, for him, is an index of the magnetic moment of the passing atom.

Each act of observation has two moments: an exchange of at least one photon with the atom, and a conscious act taking cognizance of the result. We call the whole act, the *act of observation*, and the latter part, the *conscious act of observation*. The action of the separating fields with the act of observation constitute the *full act of measurement*.

According to Heisenberg, three cases occur: – *Case I:* Observer "One" does not make an observation. The entire experimental set-up is then considered to be an isolated system and consequently to be in possession of a pure case wave function [1]. The transition probability from state "m" to state "n" in the experiment in this case is:

$$\Sigma_j \ |S_{mj}S^*_{jn}|^2 \tag{I}$$

where S_{mj} and S^*_{jn} are the matrix elements for transitions during the passage of F_1 and F_2 respectively.

We shall discuss below why it is significant for the result (I) that the observer "One" avoid interaction with the passing atom.

Case II: Observer "One" allows his apparatus to interact with the passing atom but fails to make a *conscious act of observation*. The system splits into two independent systems, annihilating the interference of probability waves, and the transition probability from "m"

---

[1] Cf. *supra*, pp. 71–76, and Appendix.

to "n" becomes in this case:

$$\Sigma_j \; |S_{mj}|^2 \; |S^*_{jn}|^2 \qquad (II)$$

A mixture is formed when the apparatus is separated from the measured object, and all correlations except the one-to-one correlation between the states of the apparatus and the states of the object are destroyed.

We shall discuss below whether and in what sense we can speak of the transformation of a pure case into a mixture apart from the two stages in the act of observation, or apart from the communication of the result to others.

Case III: Observer "One" observes that the state of the passing atom is "j", and communicates his knowledge. The total transition probability from state "m" to state "n" is in this case:

$$|S^*_{jn}|^2 \qquad (III)$$

The difference in form between (I) and (II) shows that some difference exists between Case I and Case II. The difference is in the transformation of the pure case into a mixture at the intermediate position in Case II. Heisenberg implies that the transformation from the pure case into a mixture is a physical effect – like the filtering of a liquid – and is produced by the "partly undefined interactions of the measuring apparatus" [1]. He assumes that the difference in Case II is *prior* to the conscious act of observation. It is clear that he wishes thereby to save the public objectivity of quantum mechanics. Note that Heisenberg regards the "reduction of the wave packet" – which is the final result of the measuring-process – as occurring in two steps: (1) the formation of the mixture, which is prior to the act of observation, and (2) the act of observation which ascertains or "registers" which of the possible states has been actualised [2]. We shall be concerned in the next sub-section with the question, in what sense the formation of the mixture is a physical process like the filtering of a liquid, and in what sense it is dependent on whether or not the observer-scientist makes a conscious act before or after the measurement.

---

[1] Heisenberg, *Niels Bohr* etc., p. 23; also *Physical Principles* etc., p. 60.

[2] Commenting on Einstein's thought-experiment of the semi-transparent mirror, Heisenberg says that "the experiment at the position of the reflected wave packet, exerts a kind of action (reduction of the wave packet) at the distant point occupied by the transmitted packet, and one sees that this act is propagated with a velocity greater than that of light", *Physical Principles* etc., p. 39.

The Private World of the Observer

The philosophy of complementarity, which supplies the language for quantum physics, often makes it difficult to ascertain whether a *physical process* is one that can be pictured in one or other of the complementary pictures (i.e., in the wave or in the particle picture), or as the abstract mathematical representation of this, or as its noumenal correlate (if it has one), or, finally, as the concrete empirical result of an act of observation, viz., as an event in space and time, the observed outcome of experimental activity.

One might think that, in the experiment we described above, the perturbation producing the mixture should consist in the action of the separating fields which channel the different states into separated beams. It is not, however, a sufficient explanation of the formation of the mixture since, even when separated from one another, the beams retain the intercorrelation (resulting from the superposition of many states) characteristic of a pure case. We are forced to conclude that the separating fields do not explain the formation of the mixture. *The choice of the individual observer to make a certain kind of observation is essential to the formation of a mixture.*

Heisenberg is aware of this; for he occasionally attributes the "reduction of the wave packet" to the fact that the observer has made a conscious act. The "reduction of the wave packet" is a discontinuous change in the mathematical representation not explained by the dynamical equations; it makes actual some state which before was only potential [1]. One of the more common meanings of *actuality* or *reality* for Heisenberg is "the object of everyday experience *in so far as this is actually experienced*". It is what we called *phenomenal reality* [2]. In this case, the parallelism between reality and the object of empirical observation becomes an identity, with the consequence that the "reduction of the wave packet" is identically a change in reality and a change in the object of knowledge. "To be" and "to be perceived" are not really distinguished, but they become two moments within the act

---

[1] Heisenberg, *Niels Bohr* etc., pp. 26–27.

[2] Berkeley's name is frequently mentioned in connection with the philosophy of complementarity; for example, Abner Shimony, "The Role of Observer in Quantum Theory", *Am. Jour. Phys.*, xxxi (1963), 755–773; P. K. Feyerabend, "Complementarity", in *Proc. Arist. Soc., Suppl. Vol.*, xxxii (1958), 75–104; K. Popper, "Three Views concerning Human Knowledge", *Conjectures and Refutations*, (London: Routledge and Kegan Paul, 1963); I. J. Good in *The Scientist Speculates*, pp. 301–302. A. Landé and others have pointed out that Heisenberg uses "state" to mean indifferently "the physical state of an object" and "the state of knowledge of an observer who knows quantum mechanics", *Current Issues* etc., ed. by Feigl and Maxwell, p. 355.

in which the observer-subject interacts with the object and undergoes a *prise de conscience* of this experience. If this interpretation is to be consistent, then the point of division (or *Schnitt*) on the connected chain of physical processes which unites the object to the observing subject must be capable of being displaced arbitrarily. Whether this point lies outside the body of the observer-subject or inside it should be immaterial to the physical result [1].

Logically implied in Heisenberg's view of the measuring process is the position that the behaviour and pattern of objects in human empirical consciousness are also subject to quantum mechanical laws. Acts are specified by their objects. If then the object of empirical consciousness is *identical* with reality, and if reality is subject to the quantum theory, then the behaviour and pattern of objects in human empirical consciousness is also subject to quantum mechanical laws. The quantum theory then takes on the character of a universal explanation for physical *and mental* events [2]. Von Neumann is quite explicit on this point: "It is a fundamental requirement of the scientific viewpoint – the so-called principle of psycho-physical parallelism – that it must be possible so to determine the extraphysical process of the subjective perception as if it were in reality in the physical world" [3].

Returning to the difference between Case I and Case II: let us state the dilemma in the following way [4]. If observer "One" makes an observation but fails to communicate its result, what, he might ask, is the correct state of the passing atom? Observer "Two" is in a quandary. He does not know whether to treat the case as (a) a pure case of the total isolated system (including observer "One" in the isolated system), or (b) whether to suppose that a mixture was formed at the intermediate stage. The orthodox physicist says that the latter (b) is the correct alternative. However, if observer "One" were replaced by a non-conscious piece of apparatus, then the orthodox physicist would say that the former (a) is the correct solution. Wigner says of this dilemma: "The argument for the difference in the roles of inanimate observation tools and observers with a consciousness – hence for a

[1] Heisenberg, *Niels Bohr* etc., p. 27; also von Neumann, *Mathematical Foundations* etc., pp. 418–420.
[2] Cf. E. P. Wigner, "Remarks on the Mind-Body Problem", *The Scientist Speculates*, pp. 284–301; Abner Shimony, *Am. Jour. Phys.*, xxxi (1963), pp. 755–773.
[3] Von Neumann, *Mathematical Foundations* etc., pp. 418–419.
[4] We are adapting for the purposes of our example Wigner's treatment of a similar problem and discussed by him in his article referred to in note 2 above. Cf. also, "*Theorie der quantenmechanischen Messung*", *Physikertagung, Wien, 1961* (Mosbach/Baden: 1962), p. 1; "The Possibility of a Self-reproducing Unit", in *The Logic of Personal Knowledge* (Glencoe, III: 1961), p. 231.

violation of physical laws where consciousness plays a role – is entirely cogent so long as one accepts the tenets of orthodox quantum mechanics in all their consequences" [1]. Wigner then concludes (1) that Mind is not subject to quantum mechanical laws (This is a significant break with parallelism!); (2) that the Mind can influence the course of nature by its acts, and (3) that the linear mathematical equations of the quantum theory are unsatisfactory [2].

It has often been pointed out that the epistemology of the "orthodox" interpretation leads to *solipsism;* for if the private act of observation specifies reality by actualising its potentialities and suppressing correlations, then the only possible explanations of the public objectivity of science are a pre-established harmony between minds, or that there is just one subject identical with all subjects. The first solution raises the problem of how the harmony is pre-established, e.g., by causal influences between different subjects, or by the possession of similar *a priori* forms of knowledge, etc.[3]. Reasons of simplicity and economy have commended at least in theory the second solution, viz., *solipsism,* to many physicists [4].

These are conclusions to which many quantum physicists have come not without a considerable amount of uneasiness [5]. The increasing volume of literature on the subject witnesses, if not always to these misgivings, at least to the feeling that the foundations of quantum mechanics needs some maintenance and repair [6]. Some physicists, like Ludwig in his most recent paper [7], think that the validity of quantum

---

[1] Wigner, *The Scientist Speculates*, p. 294

[2] *Ibid.*, pp. 294–298.

[3] For example, P. A. Moldauer writes: "The way in which the mind reacts to information about the physical world – and hence the structure of the wave function and of physical theory in general – would have to be regarded as strongly conditioned by the evolutionary, cultural and perhaps personal factors which strongly influence the structure of the human mind", *Am. Jour. Phys.*, xxxii (1964), p. 172.

[4] For example, Wigner, *The Scientist Speculates*, p. 290; and the remarks of the general editor pp. 301–302; also Abner Shimony, *loc. cit.*

[5] E. Schrödinger was the first to draw attention to this aspect of the "orthodox" theory of measurement in "Die gegenwärtige Lage in der Quantenmechanik", *Naturwissen.*, xxiii (1925), pp. 807–812. Another disturbing consequence of the quantum theory of measurement is the fact that in the absence of observations, the total entropy of the system does not change; it changes however discontinuously after an observation.

[6] For example, besides the articles referred to in notes we might mention the following important articles: P. K. Feyerabend, "Problems in Microphysics", in *Frontiers of Science and Philosophy* ed. by R. G. Colodny and C. G. Hempel (London, Allen and Unwin, 1964); H. Margenau, "Measurements and Quantum States", *Phil. Sci.*, xxx (1963), 1–16, 138–157; H. Margenau and R. N. Hill, *Progr. Theor. Phys.*, xxvi (1961), p. 727; Y. Abaronov and D. Bohm, *Phys. Rev.*, cxxii (1961), p. 1649; A. Landé, *Zeit. f. Physik*, clxii (1961), pp. 410, 558; the articles by Landé, Teller, Born, Bopp and Ludwig in *Werner Heisenberg und die Physik unserer Zeit* (Braunschweig: 1961).

[7] G. Ludwig, *Werner Heisenberg* usw., pp. 150–181.

mechanical laws should be restricted to the microscopic domain. Others, among whom are Heisenberg and Wigner, defend its universal validity and draw, what to them is the logical consequence, an immanentist philosophy.

Solution of the Problem

To escape the immanentist tendencies for which Heisenberg and many physicists claim to find support in the structure of quantum mechanics itself, we shall offer our own solution of the key problem placed by the difference between Case I and Case II.

It belongs to the scientist to choose the problem he wishes to consider by choosing the subject matter of the problem. This is an act of the scientist which precedes all the other acts – whether of calculation or of measurement or of observation. It is the bringing to bear of a noetic intention on something that is given or to be given in experience, namely, publicly communicable data. These constitute the subject matter of the problem, and are specified by the experimental procedures or contexts appropriate to the case under consideration. The difference in form between formula (I) and formula (II) indicates that different ensembles of data are described by the two formulae, and different experimental contexts are envisaged. The problem lies in interpreting where, among the conditions listed in the text, or presupposed by these, the difference lies.

According to the Heisenberg of the *Physical Principles of the Quantum Theory*, the difference is due to the conversion of the pure case into a mixture at the intermediate position, and is caused by the undefined interactions of the apparatus of observer "One" without, however, observer "One" making a conscious act of observation. According to Wigner, it is due to the conscious act of observation.

Neither of these solutions is satisfactory. In the first case, the theory predicts that, although the intermediate interactions are undefined, and although their effect can be reduced to vanishing point by allowing the beams to separate, the correlations characteristic of the pure case will continue unless an observation is made. In the second case, it is difficult to see how the merely noetic act of becoming aware of a particular state of the apparatus can suppress, as Wigner believes, a physical link (expressed by the superposition correlations) operative in nature.

The answer probably lies somewhere between the two views just criticised. The conversion from a pure case to a mixture is not a physical change in nature but a *logical operation* and results from the choice to consider one kind of problem rather than another. It is thus logically prior to all other acts, whether of calculation, measurement or observation. Still in the logical order, this choice is followed by the calculation of the mixture from the mathematical equations of the appropriate pure case. The corresponding activities in the experimental order are the erection of or attention to appropriate apparatus: – in Case I for observer "Two" alone, and in Case II for both observers "One" and "Two".

Consider now the two cases separately. In case I, the ensemble of data is composed entirely of the results recorded by observer "Two". In Case II, there are two independent subsensembles of data; one set recorded by observer "One" and the other set recorded by observer "Two". Heisenberg has stated in the conditions governing Case II that observer "One" does not record his observation but merely lets his apparatus interact with the passing atoms [1]. This protocol confuses the issue, since it is clear that the individual terms in formula (II) refer to the observations which observer "One" must be in a position to make and to communicate. In fact, each transition probability is an ideal frequency from which no finite recorded sample diverges systematically. The use of ideal rather than actual (counted) frequencies for the inter-mediate transition probabilities presupposes that if the actual results were considered (in a finite sample) only random deviations would be noted. It is in this trust in the essential validity of the ideal inter-mediate transition probabilities which is presupposed by the protocol. It is only accidental that, in the kind of problem here proposed, conscious acts of observation by observer "One" can be omitted without changing the physics of the case. The physical interaction involving an exchange of photons between the apparatus of observer "One" and the passing atoms seems, however, to be essential to the problem and explains the physical and experimental difference between Case I and Case II.

We have already pointed out that, even if the beams corresponding to the different states are separated by F_1, the pure case correlation remains, and this is responsible for the wave-like interference of the beams with one another. The greater the separation, however, the less the wave-like interference; and the less the separation the greater the wave-like interference. For, *on the one hand*, the greater the separation, the less energetic the exchange photon needed to establish the actual

---

[1] Heisenberg, *Physical Principles* etc., p. 61.

presence of an atom in a beam, and the less the consequent momentum disturbance of the atom – for the breadth of each beam is supposed to be considerable. And, *on the other hand*, the less the separation of the beam, the more energetic the exchange photon needed to establish the actual presence of an atom in a beam, and the greater the consequent momentum disturbance of the passing atom. It is just this correlation between the energy of the photon required to count the actual presence of atoms in a beam and the separation of the beams which is responsible for the physical and experimental difference between the two ensembles.

Physical perturbations occurring within the act of measurement are seen to be of two kinds. One is essential to the definition of a physical property; in the example we have chosen this corresponds to the perturbation which separates the states into different beams. It defines the manner for comparing atoms – not according to their resemblances with respect to our direct experience of them – but according to the way they behave within a controlled ensemble of physical interactions. The second kind of perturbation is that due to the act of observation which involves the exchange of at least one photon with the atomic system. It is this latter perturbation which is not accounted for in classical physics. It is, of course, present in every concrete observation but classical physics is not usually concerned with it. Nor is quantum mechanics particularly concerned with it, since, as we have shown, it can under favorable circumstances be reduced to an arbitrarily small amount – provided that the states to be distinguished are not continuous. The presence of this kind of perturbation at an intermediate stage in an atomic process can, however, change the statistical correlations between the initial conditions and the final results; this is a new and non-classical property.

In conclusion: we have shown in reply to (the early) Heisenberg that the formation of a mixture from a pure case is not produced by the physical separation of states; and in reply to Wigner, that the formation of the mixture is a logical step prior to all concrete acts of observation. We conclude then that the pure case wave function is merely a mathematical instrument with which to calculate the particular mixture appropriate to the kinds of observations envisaged by the experiment to be performed. From the arguments we have just given, we deduce that *quantum mechanics shares to the full the public objectivity of science.*

Wave Function

What then is the pure case wave function? It is, in the first place, a mathematical instrument of a higher logical order of abstraction than a mixture; that is, while a mixture is an ensemble of ideal frequencies of occurrence of values in random samples, the wave function itself represents a potential ensemble of such mixtures, one for every possible final experimental context which could be chosen. The appropriate mixture can be calculated only when the final experimental context is chosen. In the light of this interpretation the saying of Heisenberg that modern physics no longer refers to nature but to our knowledge of nature takes on a new significance [1]. If the object of quantum mechanics is taken to be the *wave function* (or the *physical state* as represented by a ray in Hilbert space) then this indeed is a *logical entity*, i.e., a mere instrument of our knowledge of nature; it is not a part of nature itself. Moreover, rejecting classical parallelism in knowledge we reject also its consequence – the notion that the wave function in configuration space or even the three-dimensional wave packet is the real object of quantum mechanics. The real object of quantum mechanics is its *strict object*. This makes its appearance, however, within the matrix of scientific method and theory and it has to be disengaged with great care if its true visage is to be seen. It will be the task of the next section to perform this operation.

In the second place, the wave function is connected directly with the experimental context in which the physical state is prepared. In a time independent system, the physical state retains its direct reference to this preparatory experimental context, i.e., it remains an eigen state of this context [2]. In the general case, however, the original state undergoes an evolution in accordance with its Schrödinger equation. Its physical state changes deterministically in time. At any instant, its state could be considered to be the eigen state of some (changing) experimental context, and this state might in principle be chosen as one of a set of basic (time dependent) vectors spanning the Hilbert space of the system. This is an interpretation of what is often called the *Schrödinger picture* of the system. It is of interest from the speculative point of view, but it is not of much practical use. We are left with the view expressed above that the pure case is primarily a mathematical instrument of a higher logical order capable of generating the set of mixtures associated with a determinate set of final

---

[1] Heisenberg, *Physicist's Conception of Nature*, p. 15.
[2] See appendix where a simple time independent case is considered.

experimental arrangements. Only when the final experimental context
is chosen is the physicist in possession of a formula (namely, a mixture)
which refers directly to concrete physical reality, i.e., to the verifiable
behaviour of physical things. The mixture then represents essentially
a correlation between a certain initial (or preparatory) experimental
context and a definite final one. The peculiar properties of the wave
function, e.g., its characteristic wave-like properties, is then to be
explained by the way different matrices of transition probabilities
(between initial and final states) are mathematically connected.
Landé has shown that the law of interference of probabilities is identical
with the law of unitary transformation of magic squares of transition
probabilities when certain very reasonable symmetry conditions are
fulfilled [1]. While we do not wish to pass judgement on the epistemological assumptions behind Landé's polemic against the Copenhagen
School, we think that his search for a realistic interpretation of
quantum mechanics is a reasonable one, and that his proof that the
wave function need be no more than a logical instrument connecting
an ensemble of mixtures (or an ensemble of "unit magic square
probability tables") is an important contribution to the epistemology
of quantum mechanics.

SECTION IV: FORMAL OBJECTIVITY

Formal and Public Objectivity

Public objectivity and formal objectivity differ in this respect, that
while the former is defined by public understanding, use and definition,
the latter is concerned with the part of the public object which is
affirmed to belong to the domain of being. This supposes a rather
different kind of analysis of the scientific object from that which
merely vindicates an object of knowledge from the subjectivity of
private and incommunicable experience; for even Kant could assume
that people could agree in thought, language, experience and scientific
principles without implying that the objects which they affirmed were
objects in the formal sense, i.e., belonging to the transcendent domain
of being, and he sought the *a priori* conditions of possibility of the
public object among the synthetic pure *a priori* principles which human
sensibility and understanding must possess. Public objects, then, in the

---

[1] A. Landé, *From Dualism to Unity in Quantum Physics* (Cambridge: Cambr. Univ. Press,
1960), pp. 41–54.

Kantian explanation, were subjective vis-à-vis the formal objectivity of being except that they retained a symbolic vestige of noumenal reality through their correlation with a noumenal object which, however, was otherwise unknowable.

The first stage in the treatment of formal objectivity in science will be to distinguish in the public object what belongs properly to the *content* of that object, and what belongs to the *method* of expressing this content, characteristic of the human scientific way of knowing. For it is only the content to which formal objectivity is attributed; while public objectivity may include both the content and the method of expressing it without too much discrimination provided a common understanding is achieved. It is not surprising then that the distinction between formal object and scientific method has been largely over-looked. The failure, however, to draw a correct line between method and object in human science leads, as we have seen, to perplexing problems in quantum mechanics, not merely on the philosophic level of interpretation but on the scientific level of public objectivity.

How is the strict object of a scientific statement to be disentangled from its public object? The public object is whatever can be commonly understood and correctly used by all. The strict object is the content of a critical scientific assertion, based upon the evidence of a process of experimental testing and verification: "Such and such is so". The content of the strict object is denoted by *such and such;* the criterion of its formal objectivity is the scientific evidence leading to the strong use of the verb *to be;* viz., "*is so*". The assertion may be a factual assertion or a theoretical assertion. If a theoretical assertion, we take it to be converted into a set of hypothetical factual statements of the type: "If appropriate data are given, then such and such is so".

The formal objectivity of a well-tested critical scientific statement can be contrasted with its correlate which is the subjectivity of a mere supposition or hypothesis. It can be contrasted also with the public but not formal objectivity of, say, a mythic explanation, which is an explanation where symbol and reality, method and object are not separated but indissolubly united. Formal objectivity is acquired only progressively by a theory as consciousness of its epistemological structure and evidence in its favour accumulate, until something approaching a definitive judgement can be made of its validity within a well-defined domain delineated by operational and observational concepts. The ultimate goal of scientific activity is the making of such definite, unconditional, and final judgements. "In the realm of the exact sciences", Heisenberg wrote, "there have always been *final solutions* for certain limited domains of experience... The word 'final'... means that there are always self-contained, mathematically representable, systems of concepts and laws applicable to certain realms of experience, in which realms they are *always valid for the entire cosmos and cannot be changed or improved*" [1].

The success, however, of this epistemological analysis of content and method is not a necessary condition of scientific progress, as the Kantian experiment has shown; for science can continue to make new discoveries and new syntheses, even when method and object are inextricably linked in the scientist's mind, and even if the meaning of "existence", "being" and "reality" are very much in doubt.

In this section, we shall try merely to separate *what is affirmed* viz., the content of the strict object in quantum mechanics, from what belongs to the human way of scientific knowing and so is *not affirmed*. We shall leave to another chapter the ontological problem of establishing the conditions under which what is correctly affirmed is truly being. We are concerned now merely with the physiognomy of the strict quantum object as *possibly* being.

Wave-Particle Duality Re-interpreted

In attacking psycho-physical parallelism for giving a false explanation of scientific method, we implied also a rejection on our part of the wave-particle duality of complementarity, which is a consequence of this view of scientific knowledge.

In rejecting the wave-particle duality of complementarity, we do not, however, wish to imply that some of the mathematical formulae should be changed or that observational results are not adequately accounted for by the theory. There may be inadequacies in the quantum theory, but we are not concerned with them here [2]. Nor do we wish to imply that wave and particle models are useless, either as supports of our thinking or as symbolic images or as heuristic clues to further investigation. The witness of a generation of physicists proves how useful these are. Nor do we imply finally that wave-particle duality should be dropped in favour of any one of the following: (a) a unitary "matter-particle" theory, as Popper, Bopp, Feynes,

[1] Heisenberg, *Physicist's Conception of Nature*, pp. 26–27 (italics our own).

[2] We have already noted above (chap. v, p. 96) that many physicists, as, for example, Wigner, Ludwig, Bohm, etc., purpose to change the form of the equations of quantum mechanics, for reasons connected with the basic epistemology of the "orthodox" interpretation.

Vigier and Landé have proposed [1]; (b) a unitary "matter-wave" theory like Schrödinger's [2]; or (c) a classical combination of "matter-waves" and "matter-particles" like de Broglie or Bohm have proposed [3]. All of these Heisenberg has explicitly rejected because motivated by what he calls the "ontology of materialism" characteristic of classical physics [4]. By a "matter-particle" we mean a bodily reality, possessing at every instant a unique set of space and momentum coordinates – whether or not these are actually and simultaneously determinable; it is then a strictly localised reality. By a "matter-wave" we mean an extended medium whose properties obey a wave equation, and vary continuously and determinately in time – whether or not the properties are simultaneously and actually determinable. It is then a non-localised bodily reality. These correspond to the two separate "pictures" of complementarity and belong to co-ordinate (three-dimensional) space. There is another kind of wave, called a *wave function*, which is not a bodily wave, but a mathematical function on a configuration space of 3n-dimensions – where n is the number of particles [5]. This latter wave does not possess *bodily objectivity*, but does possess the *public objectivity* of a scientific object.

Our view is that the "matter-particle" and the "matter-wave" are merely *real or possible observable symbols of the strict objects* of physics. They are the sensible sign of the strict object, and they serve the double purpose: (1) of being the criterion *for us* of the reality of the strict object, since through the observable symbol the physical object

[1] K. Popper, *The Logic of Scientific Discovery*, (London: 1959), chap. IX; Observation and Interpretation, ed. S. Körner, pp. 65–70; F. Bopp, *Werner Heisenberg* usw., pp. 128–149; *Ann. l'Inst. H. Poincaré*, tm. XV (1956), pp. 81–112; J. P. Vigier, *Observation and Interpretation*, pp. 71–77; I. Feynes, *Zeit. f. Physik*, CXXXII (1952), p. 81.

[2] E. Schrödinger, "Are there Quantum Jumps?", *Br. Jour. Phil. Sci.*, III (1952), pp. 109, 233.

[3] L. de Broglie, *Non-Linear Wave Mechanics* (Amsterdam: 1960); D. Bohm, *Causality and Chance in Modern Physics* (New York: 1957) pp. 68–128; *Observation and Interpretation*, pp. 33–40.

[4] Heisenberg uses the term *materialism* loosely. In the first place, he pays scant attention to the principal philosophic implication of the term, which is the exclusion of *spirit* in any but a subordinate role to *matter*. His thought is concerned principally with *mechanistic* explanations of nature. Cf. Heisenberg, *Physicist's Conception of Nature*, pp. 13–15. In the second place, he confuses *dialectical materialism* with *mechanistic materialism* and assumes wrongly that they share the same outlook on nature. Dialectical materialism, while not mechanistic, is opposed to Heisenberg's epistemology principally because it is a form of *realism* which lays claim to know physical reality *objectively*, i.e., in the context, to know it as it is in itself independently of the private subjectivity of the scientist-observer. Cf., Heisenberg, *Niels Bohr* etc., pp. 21–22; G. Wetter, *Philosophie und Wissenschaft in der Sowjetunion* (Munich: Rowohlts deutsche Enzyklopädie 67, 1958), pp. 7–38 and especially p. 37 where Heisenberg is criticised on this latter point.

[5] Heisenberg, *Physical Principles* etc., Preface.

enters our World of reality; and (2) of yielding a measure-number for the strict object, in so far as the content of the observable symbol is a numbered content. Contrariety of symbol, however, does not imply contrariety of the essential object symbolised. The consistency and formal unity of the atomic system is expressed by a non-contradictory mathematical theory. Heisenberg was aware of this, and used it to justify the paradoxical character of complementary pictures [1]. Our view in practice vis-à-vis the indeterminacy of wave and particle symbolic representations differs then very little in practice from that of Heisenberg and other complementarity physicists, but we attribute a very different epistemological significance to it.

Various Unitary Re-interpretations

Before summarising our view of the content of the strict object of quantum mechanics, we shall consider some recent opinions which try to dissolve wave-particle duality into a unitary particle theory. Bopp has proposed that the quantum mechanical object is a matter-particle with six determinate phase-space coordinates, viz., three of momentum (p) and three of position (q), only half of which at any instant are determinable [2]. This led him to experiment with various forms of non-classical statistical mechanics. The kind of object he proposed for such a theory was a virtual ensemble of "determinate but half-determinable" classical particles. He did not fully succeed. He was able, however, to prove a theorem of great value and interest which reads: "Any quantum mechanical system, pure and mixed states included, can be mapped into a statistical ensemble of particles in a certain phase-space: and hence also, every quantum mechanical process can be correlated to a movement of this ensemble" [3]. The conclusion of his research, however, was that his "determinate but half-determinable" phase-space was *not* the phase-space of quantum mechanics.

The reason for this negative conclusion is interesting; for, in some respects, Bopp's theory is a test case of Proposition (1) on scientific method [4], which is a characteristic of the early view of complementarity as it was proposed and defended by Bohr and Heisenberg.

---

[1] Cf. *supra*, chap. II, p. 37.

[2] Bopp, *Werner Heisenberg* usw., *loc. cit.*; *Observation and Interpretation*, pp. 189–196; *Ann. l'Inst. H. Poincaré*, xv (1956), pp. 81–112. Cf., Heisenberg's remarks in *Niels Bohr* etc., pp. 19–20.

[3] Bopp. *Observation and Interpretation, loc. cit.*

[4] Cf., *supra*, chap. IV, p. 57.

It will be recalled that this states that quantum mechanical variables are defined through the use of classical concepts. Bopp's theory applies this principle, to which he adds the restriction typical of the quantum theory, viz., that the classical variables should be determinable only within the limits imposed by the Indeterminacy Relations. Bopp's theory is a serious attempt to translate one aspect of the epistemology of complementarity (as explained by Bohr and Heisenberg) into a physical theory. A confirmation of this can be found in the fact Heisenberg criticised Bopp's approach merely because it lacked the symmetry between wave and particle which an "orthodox" quantum theory must have and not because this modified return to classical assumptions was contrary to the quantum theory. The failure of Bopp's theory was, then, a failure of *one aspect* of complementarity, that which links the definition of quantum mechanical variables to classical concepts.

Our own rejection of Bopp's assumptions follows clearly from the distinction we have made between *operational concepts* based upon experimental techniques, and *explanatory concepts* based upon the understanding of a set of interrelated processes. A physical property is expressed by us as a union of both types of concepts. Position and momentum share the same operational description in classical and in quantum mechanics, but they have different explanatory definitions. The non-commutation of position and momentum operators introduces an essentially new element in the explanatory definition of both: hence, the p and q of quantum mechanics *mean something different* from the p and q of classical mechanics [1]. Since the meanings are evidently related, and merge in fact in the limit of h = o, we can call them *analogous meanings* [2]. To assume, as Bopp does, that they *mean the same univocally* but that in the quantum mechanical case they are observationally indeterminate is to misunderstand the logic of scientific method. It is the same misunderstanding which leads to the perturbation theory of measurement. It is contrary to our intention, however, to minimise the value of Bopp's undertaking which has received

---

[1] This point has been stressed by N. R. Hanson in *Patterns of Discovery* (Cambridge: 1958), chap. VI and in his *Concept of the Positron* (Cambridge: 1963), chaps. IV–VIII; also by W. Büchel, in "Die Diskussion um die Interpretation der Quantenphysik", *Scholastik*, XXIX (1954) pp. 235–244, and in "Individualität und Wechselwirkung im Bereich des materiellen Seins", *Scholastik*, XXXI (1956), pp. 1–30.

[2] There are three kinds of *analogy:* metaphor, metonymy or extrinsic attribution, and intrinsic proportionality; cf., F. Selvaggi, "Le rôle de l'analogie dans les théories physiques", in *Actes du XIe Congrès Internat. de Philos.*, VI (Amsterdam-Louvain: 1953), pp. 138–143. The analogy in question in the text is most likely that of *intrinsic proportionality*.

Heisenberg's praise [1], but in our view its principal value is that it has tested, with what results we have seen, one of the basic theses of complementarity [2].

Landé, though he speaks of a unitary particle theory, does not make the mistake of defining p and q classically [3]. He accepts the quantum mechanical definition by non-commuting operators, and confines his re-interpretation to a statistical explanation of the wave function. For this reason, we are inclined to think that Landé's work is more acceptable than Bopp's because it is consistent with the present form of the quantum theory.

The Strict Object of Quantum Mechanics

We shall gather together here much that we have already said relevant to the strict object of quantum mechanics. It is our view that quantum mechanics is a new kind of physical theory in which both deterministic and statistical elements are organically and inseparably united [4].

From our general analysis of scientific method, we derive the proposition that the object in the strict sense of a physical theory is not *per se* representable in sensibility, and affects sensibility only *per accidens* through the presentation of an *observable symbol* [5]. A thing or property is *per se* representable in sensibility if, as an object of knowledge, it is essentially constituted as the subject of typical appearances or as the typical instrument for the performance by a human subject of a certain kind of external function or for the fulfilment of a human desire. A body in the strict sense, for example, and the properties of bodies are *per se* representable in sensibility. An

[1] Heisenberg writes that Bopp's theory "throws light upon the interesting relation between quantum theory and correlation statistics", *Niels Bohr* etc., p. 20.

[2] We have based our argument for the essential irreducibility of quantum mechanical systems upon the results of Bopp's research rather than upon the more famous theorem of von Neumann (*Mathematical Foundations* etc., pp. 295–313) proving the non-existence of dispersion-free ensembles in quantum mechanics, for Bopp's "determinate but half-determinable" ensemble fulfills the conditions of von Neumann's theorem, but is still conceived to be a classical, determinate ensemble. It seems, then, that von Neumann's theorem, in spite of a widespread opinion to the contrary, does not exclude the kind of "hidden variables" conceived by Bopp. For this reason, we consider the results of Bopp's research more fundamental.

[3] A. Landé, *From Dualism to Unity in Quantum Physics*, (Cambridge: 1960).

[4] The statistical elements in question refer to what in classical physics would be called a "distribution of errors".

[5] Mach, Rankine and others divided physical theories into *abstractive theories* dealing with perceptible objects, as for example, Newtonian mechanics; and *hypothetical theories* which used imperceptible hypothetical constructs, like atoms, electrons etc., We hold this distinction to be unfounded.

object of human scientific knowledge which is not *per se* representable in sensibility is *per accidens* representable in sensation, as, for example, through its observable symbol.

The proposition stated in the preceding paragraph applies both to *physical properties* and to the *subjects* of these properties, viz., to *things*. A physical property is the ground for a certain kind of inter-activity between things. Hence it founds a symmetrical thing-to-thing relation. The human way of discerning the presence of this activity, then, is to study to recognise its effects on other things; these effects when transformed, magnified or otherwise processed by instrumental arrangements are the observable symbols in which the physical property is observed. It is not excluded that a physical property may be also *per se* representable in sensibility, but it would be difficult to establish an exact correlation between a unique sensible effect and one of the well-defined properties of physics. Usually the types of sensation correlated with physical properties are vague and composite. "The objective [scientific] concept of temperature", Weyl wrote, "is pretty far removed from the sense data of heat perception" [1]. The sense data, on the one hand, ground an *observational or operational concept*. The property studied in physics, on the other hand, is a thing-to-thing relation founded upon a self-correlated set of physical processes, and so is expressed by an *explanatory concept*.

If physical processes are not *per se* representable in sensibility, then neither is it necessary that the subjects which possess them should be *per se* representable in sensibility. A subject of physical properties is the common term of a set of relations founded upon interactivities between subjects. There is nothing in this definition which states whether such a subject is representable in sensation; and, if so, whether this is *per se* or *per accidens*. That the subject and its properties be somehow representable in sensibility follows from the fact that we, as human knowers, need a criterion of physical reality. As to how the subject is representable in sensation, the definition does not exclude *per se* representability. Macroscopic physical objects are represented in this way, but this does not belong to the definition of a physical object as the subject of physical properties, viz., as a thing.

Since the things which are quantum mechanical systems are not *per se* imaginable, it is not necessary to suppose that they are, or should be, representable in classical phase-space. A consequence of this is that we do not need to postulate the existence of "hidden variables"

---

[1] H. Weyl, *Philosophy of Mathematics and Natural Science*, p. 140.

to explain the statistical laws of quantum mechanics. Moreover, quantum mechanics may be essentially, though not purely as we hold, a statistical theory; but we do not need to assume that it is or should be one of a classical or stochastic type.

From our analysis of quantum mechanics as a physical theory, we derive the proposition that the *strict object of quantum mechanics* is not an idealised formula of an individual system, but *the individual and concrete instance of a physical system*. We have already shown that individual and concrete instances can only be expressed as a virtual ensemble of cases. Quantum mechanics accounts both for the similarities between members of the ensemble – this is the deterministic part of the theory – and for the divergence between these members as far as this is possible – this is the statistical part of the theory. The function of quantum mechanics as a deterministic theory is twofold: viz., to define by implicit definition the set of related processes which found the quantum physical properties, and to define the idealised formula, i.e., the wave function, to which the members of the ensemble conform *more or less* and by which the members are defined as members of the particular ensemble. The function of quantum mechanics as a statistical theory is to describe the way individual and concrete instances of the properties are distributed in an ensemble of similar systems, i.e., of systems characterised by the same wave function. Within the ensemble, individual instances are random and unsystematic with respect to the order of their occurrence, but their relative frequencies of occurrence cluster around a formula which is described by the statistical part of the theory. Since all quantum mechanical variables, including position and momentum, are defined by the deterministic part of quantum mechanics, we conclude that it is methodologically incorrect to try to construct a classical (whether deterministic or statistical) model of quantum mechanics.

Matter-Form

If neither the physical system nor its properties are *per se* representable in sensibility, what then is the structure of such an object? In the first place, the Kantian distinction between matter and form is no longer applicable; for the matter received into intuition is not incorporated *intrinsically* in the constitution of the strict object. The intuitive matter is part of the observable symbol, and so is extrinsic to the strict object as constituted an object of knowledge.

In the second place, a matter and form distinction, but *not of a*

Kantian type, is an intrinsic part of the strict object. The strict object is expressed by the content affirmed in a factual statement about an actual individual system. This content is *precise and determinate* only in so far as the individual system is expressed correctly in a definite state-function; the state-function, however, is an idealisation common to a virtual ensemble. The content is *irreducibly indeterminate* in so far as neither the future nor the past of the system can be fully reconstructed from this knowledge, but only the future and past of the virtual ensemble which the state-function concretely represents. The virtual ensemble, however, represents a precise distribution only because it too is an idealisation conceived as the limiting case of an infinite ensemble; or as an ideal norm from which large finite samples do not systematically diverge. Hence individual cases taken in their concreteness are not precisely defined or definable in quantum mechanics; and moreover the element of indeterminateness is irreducible.

A strict object with two such contradictory sets of properties cannot be a simple unity. It has a factor within it on which the similarity is grounded and it has some other factor on which the dissimilarity is grounded. Since the element of dissimilarity is irreducible to precise differences, it should be regarded rather as an openness to an indefinite multiplicity – one which is ruled by the ideal frequencies predicted by the wave function. If we call the ground of multiplicity, *irreducible matter*, and the ground of similarity, *form*, then the strict object has a matter and form structure which is intrinsic to its structure, and which is not, moreover, of the Kantian type. We shall return to this discussion in chapter IX.

Summary

The "orthodox" account of the quantum mechanical measuring-process insists on the presence of an inescapable "subjective element" in it and consequently in the heart of quantum mechanics as a physical science. We distinguish three kinds of objectivity: empirical objectivity, public objectivity and formal objectivity, to which correspond three kinds of objects; namely, empirical objects, public objects and objects in the strict or formal sense. Empirical objectivity is the characteristic of an object of classical physics; public objectivity is the characteristic of an object of science, and formal objectivity is the characteristic of Being as known. We defend the public objectivity of quantum mechanics, and then attempt to separate in the public physical object the elements which belong respectively to human scientific method, and to the content of the object in the strict sense. We show that the division between causal (or deterministic) theory and statistical theory is one of human scientific method, and that quantum mechanics is a new kind of theory in which both kinds of theories are united organically and inseparably. The reason for this is that quantum mechanics takes as its object in the strict or formal sense the individual instance of an ideal norm; that is, reality in its concrete manifestations. We infer, moreover, an intrinsic matter-form structure in the strict object of quantum mechanics.

CHAPTER SIX

CLASSICAL MECHANICS AND QUANTUM MECHANICS

SECTION I: QUANTUM AND CLASSICAL ANALOGUES

Classical Analogue of Quantum Mechanics

The discussion begun in the preceding chapters raises the further question of how quantum mechanics is related to classical mechanics. We have insisted that quantum mechanical variables are differently defined from those of classical physics, not only because of the non-commutation of operators, but also because quantum mechanics includes in an organic way the functions of both a deterministic and statistical classical theory. Quantum and classical physics, and the variables appropriate to each are analogous to one another. We shall now examine the analogues which exist between these two branches of physics, and explain in what way classical mechanics is a limiting case of quantum mechanics.

From the differences in theoretical structure between classical mechanics and quantum mechanics, it is clear that the classical numerical variable cannot be the analogue of the quantum mechanical operator, for the quantum mechanical operator represents an individual measurement. The analogue of the quantum mechanical operator (applied to a particular state function) is a *concrete instance of a classical variable*. The classical numerical variable, as we have already explained, represents not a concrete instance, but an ideal norm or mean from which concrete values do not systematically diverge. No set of measured values of mass, acceleration and force obeys, with infinite precision, Newton's mechanical laws, for Newton's Laws belong, like the whole of classical physics, to the abstract and ideal, and not to the concrete. It is otherwise with quantum mechanics, for it is precisely individual and concrete instances which are envisaged. These are envisaged, however, as a virtual ensemble, that is, each instance is considered concretely as a *sample of one* chosen at random from a set of similar states. In classical mechanics the virtual ensemble is replaced by a single mean value; in quantum mechanics the actual instances, or, more exactly, the frequency of random instances, of the same type are retained. Quantum mechanics, through the matrix form of its operator and of its state-function (or state vector), deals simultaneously with the spectrum of eigen values and their ideal frequencies of occurrence. The correct classical analogue of quantum mechanics is, consequently, a theory formed by substituting for the numerical variables of classical mechanics commuting operators and for the idealised classical particle a virtual ensemble of concrete individual classical particles. The classical analogue of quantum mechanics is not Newtonian particle mechanics, but a statistical theory of classical particles with a built-in "theory of errors".

Alternatively, the same classical analogue of quantum mechanics would be obtained directly from quantum mechanics by letting h (Planck's constant) tend to zero, retaining at the same time the correspondence rules of quantum mechanics [1]. This leads to the well-known Liouville's equation for classical mechanics, viz.,[2]

$$\frac{\partial}{\partial t} f(p, q, t) = -\frac{\partial H}{\partial P} \cdot \frac{\partial f}{\partial q} + \frac{\partial H}{\partial q} \cdot \frac{\partial f}{\partial p}$$

where $f(p, q, t)$ is the probability density of the virtual classical ensemble.

In the early days of the quantum theory both Heisenberg and Bohr spoke much of *Korrespondenzdenken* without ever defining precisely what this meant. *Korrespondenzdenken* (or the Correspondence Principle) claimed to regulate the relation between classical and quantum physics. In recent years, however, the nature and even the existence of a Correspondence Principle has been much disputed. For that reason, we shall devote the following section to it.

SECTION II: THE CORRESPONDENCE PRINCIPLE

Various Uses

According to Heisenberg, Bohr and other representatives of "ortho-dox" quantum physics, quantum physics is related to classical physics

---

[1] In this chapter a *correspondence rule* is taken to be a rule for interpreting the mathematical formalism of a physical theory in *operational* or *observational* terms. Other names in use are "epistemic rules", "rules of interpretation", etc. There is no connection between *correspondence rules* and the *Correspondence Principle*.

[2] E. Wigner, *Phys. Rev.*, XL (1932), p. 42; Cf. also F. Bopp, *Werner Heisenberg und die Physik unserer Zeit*, p. 136; L. de Broglie, *Non-Linear Wave Mechanics*, pp. 166–170.

through the *Correspondence Principle*. What is the Correspondence Principle?

The Correspondence Principle is fundamentally the statement that quantum physics should be consistent with classical physics and that the results of quantum physics should pass *in some way* into classical results in limiting cases [1]. However, there are many different views about what precisely is the essence of the Correspondence Principle. It has even been said that no such principle exists, that it is simply the name given to the *clue* which helped Bohr and Heisenberg to find an acceptable generalisation of classical physics [2]. Heisenberg himself nowhere formulates the Correspondence Principle in precise language, but he allows himself to be guided now by one form, now by another, all of which reflect different applications of what he means yb *Korrespondenzdenken*. The following are five of the principal formulations of the Correspondence Principle used or implied by Heisenberg in his work.

(a) The correct form of the quantum mechanical equation is suggested by the classical analogue of the quantum problem. For example, the general prescription for quantising a classical Hamiltonian is to substitute a linear quantum operator for each of the classical variables [3].

(b) Because of the statistical interpretation of quantum mechanics, the expectation values of dynamical variables, in the time-dependent case, should obey classical laws [4].

(c) *Usually but not always*, the formulae of the quantum theory should pass over into the corresponding classical formulae whenever h (Planck's constant) can be neglected [5],

(d) *Usually but not always*, the formulae of the quantum theory should pass over to the corresponding classical formulae whenever the

---

[1] "The Correspondence Principle... postulates a detailed analogy between the quantum theory and the classical theory appropriate to the mental picture employed. This analogy does not merely serve as a guide to the discovery of formal laws..., it also furnishes the interpretation of the laws", Heisenberg, *Physical Principles* etc., p. 105; cf. also P. A. M. Dirac, *The Principles of Quantum Mechanics* (Oxford: 1958), p. 84; G. Ludwig, *Die Grundlagen der Quantenmechanik* (Berlin: 1954), chap. I; N. R. Hanson, *Concept of the Positron*, chaps. IV–VIII.

[2] For example, P. K. Feyerabend writes: "no proof is yet available to the effect that *existing* theories contain the classical point mechanics as a special case", "Problems in Microphysics", in *Frontiers of Science and Philosophy*, p. 251.

[3] Cf., note [1] above; also Heisenberg, *Physical Principles* etc., p. 105; Dirac, *loc. cit*, p. 84.

[4] Heisenberg, *Physical Principles* etc., pp. 89, 94–95, 37–38; Dirac, *loc. cit.*, p. 121.

[5] Heisenberg, *loc. cit.*, p. 101; Weyl, *Philosophy of Math.* etc., pp. 185–186; Dirac, *loc. cit.*, p. 87; that the principle is not universal was pointed out by Bohr in *Atomic Theory and the Description of Nature*, p. 87.

quantum numbers are large and the spacing between the eigenvalues is negligible, as, for example, when the size of the system is large [1].

(e) In marginal cases between micro- and macrodomains, both the quantum theory and the classical theory should be valid; and to the extent that the theoretical formulae represent the same act (or acts) of measurement or observation the values predicted by both theories should agree [2].

The variety of formulations of the Correspondence Principle is derived from the variety of uses made of it by Heisenberg and other classic authors of the quantum theory. Let us assume that there is one which is more basic than the others and capable of founding all the others; then it is evident from the non-necessary character of (c) and (d) that these are secondary and derived principles. Principle (a) generally results in (b), but (b) must be regarded as more basic than (a); for in the case of a clash between (a) and (b), it is (a) that would have to yield. However, as (b) applies only to time-dependent cases and the quantum theory is often and even principally concerned with stationary states, we do not think that (b) is sufficiently broad.

Principle (e) states a certain material correspondence of the quantum theory with classical theory when applied to marginal cases. The condition is not primarily one of continuity of form but of continuity of subject matter, and continuity of certain results. As the nature of a marginal case makes it impossible to distinguish sharply in it *quantum* from *classical* subject-matter, (e) must be regarded as a necessary consequence of the demand for the consistency of results in physics. Moreover, the requirement that, where theoretical formulae correspond (through correspondence rules) with the same act (or acts) of measurement, the predicted values should agree, implies a certain continuity of form too. The continuity of form is not a mere symbolic analogy (though this may provide a valuable clue) but the practical agreement of results, taking into account *possibly different symbolic forms and different correspondence rules*. Moreover, if (e) holds, then (b) also holds in the marginal domain, for in this case the quantum wave packet cannot be much greater than the size of the marginal object, and consequently the expectation values of its dynamical variables based upon a sampling of an ensemble of independent cases will be a good estimate of the classical dynamical variable: the classical variable,

---

[1] Heisenberg, *loc. cit.*, pp. 83, 116; that the principle was not universal was pointed out by Bohr, *loc. cit.*, pp. 69–70, 85.

[2] Implied in Heisenberg, *loc. cit.*, pp. 66, 105, 107; and by Bohr, *loc. cit.*, pp. 14, 18, 37, 72; and by Dirac, *loc. cit.*, p. 84. Cf. also Heisenberg, *Philosophic Problems* etc., p. 24.

as we have repeatedly said, is itself an ideal norm like an expectation value. Also, if (e) holds, then both (c) and (d) hold in those cases where the theoretical quantum formulae represent the same acts of measurement as the corresponding classical formulae. This last condition, moreover, specifies when and under what circumstances (c) and (d) hold, and also when they do not hold. Principle (e) allows us to respect the *difference in symbolic form* and the *difference in correspondence rules*, and at the same time to specify clearly how two such different physical theories can correspond in some principle.

We propose then to regard (e) as the most basic and fundamental expression of the Correspondence Principle. From the logical point of view, the domain of correspondence between classical and quantum physics, which we described as that of "marginal subject matter", is defined in terms of activities, events and data presented and described in the World of observations, and hence possessing a *reality* independently of which of the two theories is chosen to explain them [1].

SECTION III: COMPLETENESS OF QUANTUM MECHANICS

Completeness Principle

Closely connected with the Correspondence Principle is the problem of the completeness of quantum mechanics as an explanation of physical systems. The *Completeness Principle* in question is one which affirms the sufficiency of a complete set of commuting variables to provide the maximum amount of information about a system. It does not say that we know when a set of such variables is exhaustively complete. The principle concerns rather the exclusion from the members of a complete set of any variable which is conjugate to a member of the set. Physicists sometimes speak also of the *observational completeness* of a physical theory, meaning the ability to construct apparatus to correspond with any given Hermitian operator – for an arbitrary Hermitian operator is thought to define an observable. The observational completeness of the quantum theory is, according to Feyerabend, "not far from being a myth" [2]. However, this is really of little importance since, unlike the supporters of *operationalism* (and presumably Feyerabend here?), we do not hold that *observables* are generalisations of experimental procedures, but that they are the

---

[1] N. R. Hanson expresses almost the same idea in *Patterns of Discovery*, p. 156.
[2] Feyerabend, "Problems of Microphysics", *Frontiers of Science and Philosophy*, p. 251.

explanations why certain experimental procedures are measurements of a single property and others are not.

The quantum mechanical state function is unambiguously defined by a *complete set of commuting variables*. This set contains only one of every pair of non-commuting variables; for example, if one chooses to specify the state-function of a system by the position variable, then its momentum does not enter directly into its specification at all [1]. A complete set of commuting variables describes the number of independent dynamical degrees of freedom of a physical system, and hence the number of initial conditions which must be known if the system is to be described with the degree of completeness permitted by the theory. It would at first sight appear that classical mechanics gives a more complete explanation of the physical system than quantum mechanics, since the number of independent dynamical degrees of freedom considered by classical mechanics is larger. Heisenberg and the majority of quantum physicists, however, have always defended the position that the quantum theory is the more general and complete physical theory. This was the subject of the first major debate between quantum physicists of the Copenhagen School and representatives of the classical viewpoint which took place at the Fifth Physical Conference of the Solvay Institute at Brussels in October ,1927 [2]. Bohr and Einstein were the principal participants and the discussion continued fitfully for many years. The debate was to a certain extent inconclusive and in recent years it has been revived with renewed vigour [3].

The problem under discussion can be restated in the following way: assuming that quantum mechanics is valid *universally* in the physical domain, does it include *everything* which an explanation according to classical mechanics would give? Heisenberg, Bohr and the majority of physicists answer: Yes! Einstein and a small group of physicists say: No!

The principal difficulty is to explain why the quantum mechanical

---

[1] Since a quantum mechanical system represents and is represented by a virtual ensemble, the position variable is specified when the wave function is given; this however leads to a probability density for all possible values. The momentum enters *indirectly* in this specification since, by a Fourier transform, one can pass from the coordinate representation to the momentum representation.

[2] Niels Bohr gives a detailed account of this debate in *Albert Einstein: Philosopher-Scientist*, ed. by P. A. Schilpp, pp. 201–241.

[3] For example: A. Landé, *From Dualism to Unity in Quantum Physics* (Cambridge: 1960); *Foundations of the Quantum Theory, A Study in Continuity and Symmetry*, (New Haven: 1955); D. Bohm, *Causality and Chance in Modern Physics*, (Princeton: 1957); L. de Broglie, *Non-Linear Quantum Mechanics* (Amsterdam: 1960), as well as a vast literature some of which was referred to on p. 96, note 6.

description of a system does not always pass over into its expected classical description when h (Planck's constant) tends to zero. Although the quantum theory is a "rational generalisation of the causal space-time description of classical physics, this view does not mean, however, that classical electron theory may be regarded simply as the limiting case of a vanishing quantum of action" [1]. Einstein, for example, considered the case of a small perfectly elastic sphere of "marginal" size, bouncing back an forth between two parallel and perfectly elastic walls. The quantum mechanical description is a stationary state in which the probability of finding the ball at any position is a constant [2]. Allowing h to tend to zero does not yield the classical description of a ball moving continuously back and forth between the walls.

We answer Einstein's difficulty by pointing out that the difference between classical and quantum mechanics is not merely the finite size of Planck's constant, but also the correspondence rules. If we let h tend to zero in quantum mechanics while *retaining the same correspondence rules*, we arrive at a classical statistical analogue of the physical system – and not at the classical mechanical description of an individual system. In this respect, Einstein's objection to the claim that classical (deterministic) mechanics is a particular case of quantum mechanics is a valid one. The difference, as Einstein showed, is especially striking when the quantum mechanical system is taken to be in a stationary state. The classical analogue of this situation (when the only change involved is the neglect of h) is a Gibb's ensemble composed of a system with a ball which at any time could be found anywhere between the reflecting walls with equal probability. The formulae in the quantum mechanical case go over into corresponding formulae in the classical statistical case.

However, if with the neglect of Planck's constant we also change the correspondence rules so as to associate with each (now commuting) operator the average of a series of measurements made within a small interval of time at a definite epoch – this is the measure of the classical value – then the case is no longer time independent, and, by Ehrenfest's theorem, we arrive at the corresponding classical equations of a single particle.

Again, admitting as we do that the quantum mechanical description is a statistical one, we open ourselves to Einstein's principal objection

[1] N. Bohr, *Atomic Theory* etc., p. 87.
[2] A. Einstein, "Elementare Ueberlegungen zur Interpretation der Grundlagen der Quantenmechanik", in *Scientific Papers Presented to Max Born*, pp. 33–40.

to the comprehensive claims of quantum mechanics, that it does not describe the individual system and so its description is *incomplete*. Einstein writes: "Quantum mechanics describes a collectivity of systems, not the individual systems. The description by means of the psi-function is in this sense an incomplete description of the single system, not a description of a real state" [1]. The objection is a classical statement of the rationalist viewpoint.

We have already elaborated our answer in the preceding chapters. We may summarise it as follows. A description of a virtual ensemble (through a probability law) is not necessarily an incomplete description of the individual; but it is our way of knowing the individual, with reference first of all to an ideal norm (determining the character of the instances), and then with reference to the relative frequency of deviations from the norm. This is the invariant structure of our scientific knowing. It is found in quantum physics, and also, though in a less obvious way, in classical physics. What Einstein called the "real objective physical description" of single mechanical systems in classical mechanics is non-statistical only to the extent that the description is ideal and abstracts from all actual, existing and individual cases; and it describes any actual individual case only to the extent that the equations of classical mechanics are united to a statistical "theory of errors" and are, to this extent, in the terminology of classical physicists, "non-objective" [2].

Einstein, Podolsky and Rosen had already formulated the same objection, supporting their arguments by a very clever deduction from the very formalism of quantum mechanics itself [3]. They showed that, while experimentally the position and momentum of a particle cannot be measured exactly at the same instant, quantum mechanics allowed – and in fact seemed to require in some cases – that they should have definite values *in principle* even independently of the act of observation. They concluded that the quantum mechanical description of concrete cases was incomplete. The argument was based upon Einstein's famous definition of "physical reality": "If without in any way disturbing a system, we can predict with certainty the value of a physical quantity, then there exists an element of physical reality corresponding to this physical quantity" [4].

[1] Einstein, *ibid.*, p. 40.
[2] Max Born has stressed this fact in *Science*, cxxii (1955), pp. 675–679, and in *Werner Heisenberg* usw., pp. 103–118.
[3] A. Einstein, B. Podolsky, N. Rosen, "Can Quantum Mechanical Description of Physical Reality be Considered Complete?", *Phys. Rec.*, xl (1935), p. 777.
[4] *Ibid.*

As a definition of the reality of physical properties, it is open to the following criticisms. *In the first place*, the physical properties of an actually existing system are defined through interactions with other systems within appropriate measuring processes. We have shown that this is an essential part of what is described by physics and cannot be omitted without idealising reality. Hence, Einstein's conclusion that a quantum particle should have, independently of the measuring process, six determinate phase-space coordinates, is not a statement about individual existing systems, but about a certain idealised model (viz., the classical particle model) of them. We might add that while the conscious act of observation is not constitutive of the *meaning* of reality – and to this extent we can agree with Einstein – still, the physical property is defined in relation to an interaction (viz., a measuring interaction) *even though* the outcome may not be consciously observed. For us, the conscious act of observation is only a *criterion* – but a necessary one – of the reality *for-us* of a physical property or system.

In the second place, implied in Einstein's definition is the rationalistic supposition that it belongs to the definition of reality, that a physical property has a definite and precise measure-number *to an infinity of decimal places*. We hold that this is false for the following reasons: (a) a precise number is always an ideal norm and represents a constructed rule through which we understand many instances in one concept; (b) the measure-number does not belong formally to the physical property but to its observable symbol (which is found formally in the measuring instrument) and naturally only in so far as this is numbered; (c) a numbering is the application of a humanly constructed set of conventional symbols which are conceptual instruments for expressing physical relationships, and such notions as continuity, limit, irrational number, derivative, etc., belong rather to the conceptual instrument as such than to what is represented concretely by the instrument. We concur with J. L. Synge who has remarked: "When properly understood (i.e., as mathematicians understand them) these concepts exist in the human mind and not in nature; it is a meaningless waste of time to debate whether the ratio of two measured lengths is rational or irrational, or whether matter is continuous or discontinuous, because the concepts of irrationality and continuity belong to the world of the intellect, a world of mathematics, and not to the real world in which phenomena occur and are measured by pieces of apparatus" [1].

[1] J. L. Synge, *Relativity: The Special Theory* (Amsterdam: 1958), p. 164.

Summary

Accepting the view that quantum mechanics is validly applicable wherever classical mechanics is applicable, it becomes necessary to explain how they are related to one another. Whenever Planck's constant (h) can be neglected (i.e., when position commutes with momentum) there is a twofold classical analogue of the quantum mechanical system: (a) if the correspondence rules of quantum mechanics are retained, then the classical analogue is a classical statistical theory; and (b) if the correspondence rules are changed to link the operators with a value averaged over a small time interval, then the operator is effectively replaced by a numerical variable and classical particle mechanics is obtained. The ambiguity in the kind of limiting process leading from quantum mechanics to classical mechanics is reflected in the variety of opinions about the nature of the *Correspondence Principle*. After an analysis of various opinions, we conclude that the most basic formulation of the Correspondence Principle refers to the continuity of formulae when applied to marginal matter, taking into account the differences in correspondence rules between a typical classical theory and quantum mechanics. We then examine the *Completeness Principle* attacked by Einstein and show that a satisfactory solution of the Einstein-Podolsky-Rosen paradox depends upon the epistemological analysis made in the preceding chapters.

PART II

REALITY IN QUANTUM MECHANICS

THE ONTOLOGICAL STRUCTURE OF ATOMIC SYSTEMS

CHAPTER SEVEN

VARIOUS THEORIES OF REALITY IN PHYSICS

SECTION I: INTRODUCTION

Science and Ontology

Part II on the ontology of quantum mechanics follows Part I both logically and, in our case, chronologically. It follows logically since it is our aim to disentangle the concepts of reality and being implicit in various accounts of scientific knowing; it follows chronologically since in Heisenberg's case his explicit ontology was not formulated before 1950, that is to say, not until twenty-five years after the publication of quantum mechanics [1].

In the preceding chapters, we referred many times to the concepts of *reality* and its *criterion* implicit in various accounts of the method and object of scientific research given by different physicists [2]. In this and in the following chapters, we shall take up this question in a more systematic fashion. The aim is not to establish an ontology on the basis of scientific method but to examine critically the ontological pre-suppositions of certain physicists and notably those of Heisenberg. As Wigner points out: "The problems of epistemology and ontology have an increased interest for the contemporary physicist. The reason is, in a nutshell, that physicists find it impossible to give a satisfactory description of atomic phenomena without explicit reference to the consciousnes" [3].

We have already described this crisis from the point of view of epistemology; we shall now consider the ontological aspect. Our conclusion, as in the preceding part, will be that the dialectical opposition lies not, as Heisenberg and Wigner seem sometimes to imply, on the level of physical theory, but on the level of philosophical

---

[1] See *infra*, chap. VIII.

[2] See *supra*, chap. I, sect. I, chap. V, sec. I and elsewhere.

[3] E. P. Wigner, *Two Kinds of Reality*, lecture given at the Marquette Conference for the Philosophy of Science, Milwaukee, 1961.

presuppositions which tend to project on to the scientific plane tensions which first ought to be resolved on the pre-scientific and philosophic plane, viz., on the *plane of intentionality*. Thus the outcome of our analysis will be that quantum physics implies the necessity of a more critical revision of epistemological and ontological concepts than took place in the quantum revolution of 1925–1927. Changing the mathematical form of the quantum mechanical equations may suppress the symptoms of the tension between physics and philosophy, but this can only be a temporary measure so long as there is lacking a true harmony between philosophy and science.

Our view of such a harmony was already outlined in chapter one [1]. We reject the notion that the true harmony is established by the absorption of philosophy into science or vice versa, or by the distinction between technical science and a philosophy which is merely a *haute vulgarisation* of science. On the contrary, we point out that within the scientific enterprise there is an essential duality comprising question and answer: on the one hand, an intention constituting a scientific question and incorporating a philosophy; on the other, a neomatic response (illuminated by the light of the noetic intention) revealing that sphere of the real which physical science can attain. Philosophy is to science as the structure and justification of the specifically scientific noetic intention is to the noematic content of the scientific theory. The meaning of the latter is ascertained by reference to the former; but the former is usually latent and implicit because it is not the conscious application of a scientific philosophy, but rather a manner of treating reality, incorporated, as M. Dondeyne says [2], in a *comportement*, that is, in a way of doing scientific research which is learned by becoming apprenticed to the tradition of scientific research. Scientists can agree in practice as to what is good scientific procedure and what is not but, in order to make progress in the scientific enterprise, they generally do not have to explicitate or justify the philosophical ground of these, nor pronounce on the ontological content of their discoveries.

The disagreement in ontology springs from a number of causes, the principal one being a professional bias against a study of subjectivity. One distrusts the morsel of truth to be found by reversing the usual extroverted direction of scientific research and by seeking it instead in introspection and in the analysis of subjectivity. Besides

[1] See *supra*, chap. I, sec. I.
[2] A. Dondeyne, *Foi chrétienne et pensée contemporaine*, p. 26.

the unfamiliarity of this kind of inquiry, for which the methodology of the physical sciences gives no prescription, there is the dilemma founded upon the view that valid objective knowledge is limited to objects placed in the relation of exteriority to the knowing subject. If this were so, then it would be futile to look for objective knowledge by analysing the intentionality of the scientist as subject. Formal objectivity, which is the ultimate objective of all knowing activity, is the objectivity of the unconditionally affirmed object, that is, of being and this is not based upon the relation of exteriority.

Because of this ambiguity of mind on the part of the scientist, there is to be found a great diversity of views among them about the onto- logical content of physics. This can be traced to the underlying diversity of unanalysed views as to the *meaning* of "reality" and as to what constitutes the proper *criterion* in human knowledge for the discernment of what is real. In this chapter we shall discuss the two main philosophi- cal tendencies between which physicists to-day tend to be divided. In the next chapter, we shall situate Heisenberg within these tendencies and analyse in a more detailed fashion his explicit ontology.

SECTION II: RATIONALIST TENDENCIES

Universality and Necessity

Rationalism is the tendency to equate the meaning of *reality* with what can be expressed conceptually, i.e., with what can be defined. Since a definition always has a certain universality in so far as it can be applied normatively to an endless array of things, an essential mark of the rationalist view of reality is that it is applicable to all possible universes. Moreover, since a definition is always a synthesis of many elements (connected possibly in time), it follows that whatever falls under the definition is *necessarily* a system of elements ordered (in time) just as the definition requires; for it is of the essence of the rationalist definition to be normative. Thus, true ontological knowledge is characterised by *universality* (in all possible universes) and *necessity* (in temporal evolution). The rationalist universe is deterministic. The assertion that the aim of science is to discover the immutable, absolute normative essences of things is sometimes called *essentialism*.

We may distinguish two degrees of universality and necessity. (a) There is the definition that yields the *a priori* possibility of deducing the concrete sequence of events which comprise this universe of our experience – including the initial conditions of this universe. This goal is reminiscent of Spinoza and Leibniz, and no doubt it is the horizon towards which all physicists of strong rationalist tendencies look. Eddington, Schrödinger and the elder Einstein were fascinated by this goal of finding the universal laws of nature "from which the cosmos can be built up by pure deduction" [1]. Popper, one of the principal antagonists of this view, writes, not unjustly, of Einstein's field theory: "It might be described as a four-dimensional version of Parmenides' unchanging three-dimensional universe. For in a sense no change occurs in Einstein's four-dimensional block-universe. Everything is there just as it is, in its four-dimensioanl *locus;* change becomes a kind of 'apparent' change; it is 'only' the observer who as it were glides along his world-line and becomes successively conscious of the different *loci* along his world-line, that is of his spatio-temporal surroundings" [2]. In this view, the function exercised by sensibility is destined to wither away; for when sufficient observations have been made to formulate and verify the universal cosmic calculus or *Universal Characteristic*, sensibility will have no function left to perform. It will remain as witness of an imperfect stage which has been passed, repeating in mine a story of which the beginning, middle and end are already perfectly comprehended and irrevocably decided. Few mathematicians or physicists, however, really believe that this programme is possible. The reason is that the basic equations of physics are generally taken to be differential equations (expressing the fact that disturbances are propagated with finite speed into the surrounding environment) and differential equations generally do not yield definite solutions unless contingent initial conditions are added to them.

(b) For this reason a more common view is that the aim of physics is to arrive at the general invariant dynamic laws characteristic of all possible universes. This second view accepts the fact that this universe of ours is not exhaustively deducible; but that contingent elements enter into its specification. There is a true place and function in this view for human sensibility; for in addition to the stage of imperfect knowledge that it is, it also confers something of its own which is not obtainable by rational deduction, viz., the contingent conditions which specify a process. Verification in experience then takes on a new significance by becoming a criterion unto us as to which of the possible universes is existing and actual in our experience.

---

[1] A. Einstein, *Essays in Science* (New York: Philos. Libr., 1934).
[2] K. Popper, *Conjectures and Refutations* (London: 1963), p. 80.

However, as long as experience contributes nothing to the meaning of *reality*, the essential rationalistic thesis remains [1].

Einstein

We have already met an explicit explanation of this kind of rationalism in Einstein's criticism of the quantum theory. "Physics", he wrote in his autobiographical notes, "is an attempt *conceptually* to grasp reality as it is independently of its being observed. In this sense one speaks of 'physical reality'" [2]. The act of measurement and observation is, as we have explained, a complex activity involving an interaction between object and instrument-observer (which is essential to the definition of the physical property as a property-for-things) followed by an exchange of at least one photon between the scientist-observer and the instrument (which makes the property a property-for-us). Einstein, following the analysis of quantum physicists themselves, does not distinguish between the two stages, and so he is led to consider measurement simply as a perturbation of an object by an observer-subject. It is clear, however, that Einstein wanted to eliminate both species of relativities from our concept of reality – reference, namely, to the human sensibility of the observer-scientist, and reference to the interaction which is an inescapable element of the measuring process. The former implies that sensibility does not enter into the meaning of physical reality; the latter, that the essences of things can be known by us in a non-relative way. Both of these positions we hold to be false.

Critique

Essentialism seems to be in opposition to the provisional tentative and progressive character of physics which refuses to admit that any stage of its development may be final. A scientific explanation is a noetic system on the move towards higher syntheses and viewpoints. The tentative and provisional nature of such syntheses may be the reason that many philosophers of science of rationalist tendencies are willing to adopt a nominalist or instrumentalist view of physical science. We may cite, for example, Duhem and Poincaré.

Essentialism, besides, is contradicted by the irreducibly statistical element which enters into the application of physical laws to concrete

---

[1] See the interesting discussion of Eddington and others by E. C. Mascall in *Christian Theology and Natural Science* (London: Longmans, 1956), chap. III.

[2] *Albert Einstein: Philosopher-Scientist*, ed. by P. A. Schilpp (Evanston: Libr. of Living Phils., 1949), p. 81 (italics added).

instances and individual cases. There is, as we have seen, an epistemological reason for believing in the irreducibly statistical character
of quantum mechanical laws. Einstein, Rosen, Bohm, Vigier, de
Broglie in recent years and others refused to accept the irreducibility
of quantum mechanical laws and sought for a deeper explanation
in "hidden sub-quantum variables", etc.[1]. Our principal argument
against this view is that physical laws do not directly express what
is concrete and individual in the instances. Physical laws are ideal
norms from which concrete instances do not diverge systematically.
Although it is always possible through improved technique to improve
the expression of a law by determining its constant parameters more
accurately, the possibility of improvement does not imply that the
old law may be false. An ideal norm may be a *crude* ideal norm without
being thereby false. To falsify it would require the substitution of a
new theoretical structure for the old. This of course can happen.
However, we have good epistemological reasons for believing that a
certain irreducible statistical residue would be present even in the
new law.

On the other hand, essentialism of a less rigid kind, whether of
Hegelian or rationalist inspiration, can be a most effective partner
of theoretical science, providing it with a dynamic impulse motivated
by the hope of glimpsing the Absolute. It is one of the great motivating
forces in the construction of physical theories of a deterministic kind.
It is the undisguised heuristic intention behind many of the attempts
to replace or re-interpret the statistical structure of quantum physics
by a deterministic one based upon hidden variables, or Superstates,
or a deterministic sub-quantum level [2].

Essentialism, in so far as it is in search of a scientific explanation
free from all relativity to observers and measuring instruments,
contradicts the human manner of knowing, for the human manner
of knowing a reality, whether scientifically or non-scientifically, is
through its incorporation into a World of related things. To aspire
to know an individual essence in an absolute manner "as it is in itself"
and outside of its natural milieu, viz., a World, is to attempt the
impossible. The scientific method belongs to men and not to God
or to angelic intelligences.

Finally, as Popper, the inveterate enemy of essentialism, points out,

[1] See *supra*, chap. v, sect. iv.

[2] A *Superstate* is a hypothetical description which would give a more detailed description
of the physical system than is allowed by present-day quantum mechanics. The word was
used by H. J. Groenewold, *Physica*, xii (1948).

essentialist views have played a restrictive and obscurantist role in the history of physical ideas [1]. Perhaps the reason for this is that it overlooked something essential in the act of knowing, something that gave it, as it were, an extra degree of mental freedom. This is the participation of human sensibility in the expression of the strict object of knowledge. The first immediate effect of the quantum revolution was to dethrone pure deductive reason as a mirror of physical reality, and to put intuitive sensitive experience in its place. This brings us to the empiricist tendency in modern physics.

SECTION III: EMPIRICIST TENDENCIES

Empiricism and Quantum Mechanics

Empiricism is the tendency to identify both the meaning and criterion of *reality* with the content of empirical intuition. *To be*, then, is *to be an object actually given in perception;* and, as Berkeley pointed out, this position entails the logical denial of true and objective judgements about any reality which is not actually being perceived.

The conversion of science to empiricism after three hundred years of unrestrained rationalism led to the rediscovery of Berkeley whose ontological views are, consciously or unconsciously, accepted by the majority of quantum physicists to-day. A strongly empiricist tendency was implied in Heisenberg's great insight of 1925 that a physical reality must earn its title by being *observable*, i.e., by being given in some way in perception; and from this he drew the consequence that, although an object of knowledge is always "objective", it is "not real", except to the extent that it is actually being observed [2].

Heisenberg and Bohr single out what they believe to be the most significant discovery of the new physics, "that we are both onlookers and actors in the great drama of existence" [3]; we are onlookers in the sense that reality is out there given to us in phenomena: we are also actors since we know it only in the dramatic act of doing something to it (in the measuring process). Our conceptual schemes merely help to "reduce (the phenomena) to order" [4]. They do not tell us what reality is really like. This brings out two of the principal character-

---

[1] Popper, *loc. cit.*, p. 105.
[2] Heisenberg, *Niels Bohr* etc., p. 27.
[3] Heisenberg, *Physicist's Conception of Nature*, p. 16, who quotes from Bohr's *Atomic Physics* etc., p. 119.
[4] Bohr, *loc. cit.*, p. 1.

istics of the philosophy of the Copenhagen School of quantum physicists: (1) "Reality" is to be defined as what is given in perception
"out there" in the relation of exteriority to the subject; it is the
content of an *observation-event*, and this constitutes one of the *atomic-
reality elements* of the quantum physicist's world; (2) conceptual
schemes are merely instruments, *tools* for organising, predicting and
employing usefully sequences of observation-events.

Instrumentalism

The Copenhagen School is then frankly anti-essentialist, at least
in atomic physics; and it espouses a kind of nominalism vis-à-vis
the sciences which is often referred to by the name of *instrumentalism*.
"The central claim of the instrumentalist view is that a theory is
neither a summary description nor a generalised statement of relations
between observable data. On the contrary, a theory is held to be a
rule or a principle for analysing and symbolically representing certain
materials of gross experience, and at the same time an instrument
in the technique for inferring observation statements from other such
statements" [1]. Poincaré, although himself not an instrumentalist, was
perhaps the first to draw attention to the conventional element in
scientific theories. Type examples of instrumentalist philosophies are
the *positivism* of Mach and of the Vienna Circle, the *operationalism* of
Bridgman and the *pragmatism* of Peirce, Dewey and William James.

The rapid spread of instrumentalist views among physicists since
the discovery of quantum mechanics is partly a reaction to the failure
of classical physics and its inordinate rationalist pretensions, and
partly due to the rising influence of Mach's philosophy. This had
inspired Einstein's special theory of relativity, which was the first of
the great successes of modern physics [2]. His influence, moreover, was
certainly felt by Heisenberg and Bohr. It must be admitted that
positivism contains a true, even if over-modest, description of what
scientists *do* when they *do research*. Its claims, however, are principally
founded on the structure and rational interpretation of quantum
mechanics itself and it has focussed attention upon the subjectivity
of the observer-scientist which, in the "orthodox" view, determines
the actuality of observed empirical reality. The question has already

---

[1] E. Nagel, *The Structure of Science* (New York: 1961), p. 129.

[2] For Mach's influence on the early Einstein, cf., *Albert Einstein: Philosopher-Scientist*,
p. 53. Popper (*loc. cit.*, p. 114) refers to a conversation he had with Einstein in 1950 in which
Einstein stated that he repented of the instrumentalist interpretation he gave to the special
theory of relativity.

been treated from the logical and epistemological point of view; let us now review here the ontology presupposed in the presentation of a great modern physicist like Eugene Wigner.

Wigner

Wigner prefaces his lecture "Two Kinds of Reality" by the statement that he believes his views represent those "at which most of my fellow-physicists would arrive if they were sufficiently pressed for their opinion of the subject" [1]. He points out the impossibility of giving a description of atomic phenomena "without explicit reference to consciousness", especially to the consciousness of the observer in the final stage of the measuring process, viz., in what is called the "reduction of the wave packet".

He then describes "two kinds of reality". The first kind is the "existence of my consciousness" which contains objects of consciousness ("sensations") and the subject who is conscious ("I"): these are "absolute realities". The second kind is the "existence of everything else", e.g., books, magnetic fields, etc., which are "relative realities", "constructs" of the mind whose sole function is usefulness for guiding one's action and for communicating with other people.

Here clearly expressed are the two elements already summarised: (1) that *reality* – both subject and object – gets its primary meaning within sensation, and (2) that the function of conceptual knowledge is purely instrumental.

Critique [2]

The over-modest description of scientific activity given by instrumentalism does not explain the powerful drive and inspiration of scientific research. From the time of Galileo the scientist has always claimed to be a seeker for *what really is,* and not just for a pattern of how things *appear to be* [3]. The sudden cult of intellectual modesty

---

[1] Wigner, *loc. cit.* He says that the "quantum theory will form the background but not the basis of this analysis".

[2] A very penetrating critique of *instrumentalism* from inside the school of logical empiricism has been made by the group associated with the *Minnesota Centre for the Philosophy of Science*, as for example, Grover Maxwell's "The Ontological Status of Theoretical Entities" in *Minnesota Studies in the Philosophy of Science*, vol. III, ed. by H. Feigl and G. Maxwell (Minneapolis: Univ. of Minn., 1962), pp. 3–27; P. K. Feyerabend, "Explanation, Reduction and Empiricism", *ibid.*, pp. 28–97; also by the same author, "An Attempt at a Realistic Interpretation of Experience", *Proc. Aristot. Soc.*, LVIII (1958), pp. 144–170. We have already criticised the neglect of certain distinctions which we believe to be fundamental for an adequate realistic theory of science, e.g., properties-for-us vs. properties-for-things, observable symbol vs. property symbolised etc. Cf. *supra,* chap. IV.

[3] Galileo allowed his spokesman Salviati to exclaim: "I cannot express strongly enough

among physicists after 1925 is not the result of a critical analysis of the epistemological value of the scientific method, but rather the aftermath of the disillusionment that followed the overthrow of the dogmatic rationalism of classical physics: dogmatic rationalism was turned into dogmatic instrumentalism because this was the philosophy of Niels Bohr who, as leader of the Copenhagen School, became the official interpreter of the new and revolutionary ideas which meteor-like signalled the end of the classical era of physical science.

Instrumentalism stresses the utilitarian function of conceptual knowledge. According to its principles all concepts are expressions of thing-for-us relations, which is the general structure of everyday concepts and those of the operational and observational parts of physics. This assertion is another way of stating proposition (1) on scientific method which we criticized in chapter four.

Moreover, instrumentalism does not distinguish between the *meaning* of reality and the conceptual content which is one of the *means* through which we know it. A conceptual content may describe a reality by relating it to us, or it may explain it by relating it to other things. The concept expresses a certain kind of relationship between terms; the terms occur within the context of a systematic totality called a *World*. Hence, the discovery of the primary aspect of relativity which our conceptual knowledge has, and which instrumentalism stresses, does not eliminate formal objectivity (or reality as an absolute or as being) from "realities of the second kind". If it did, there could be no relation-to-us, and hence no systematic totality and no World to be the *locus* of the real. All of these are, in the intention of the act of knowledge, affirmed (probably or absolutely) as objective in the strict sense.

The valid element in instrumentalism is its insistence on the flexibility of the human mind in seeking and in inventing explanations not merely of one particular kind (as for example of spatial models), but of many kinds. It witnesses to a stage in the self-revelation of human consciousness in which human consciousness discovers for the first time that it is not limited to one kind of operation, but is a general principle of understanding capable of generating a bewildering diversity of acts and of originating new ones of startling novelty in response to novel situations. It is the discovery – as disquieting to the

my unbounded admiration for the greatness of mind of Aristarchus and Copernicus who conceived the heliocentric system and held it to be true... in violent opposition to the evidence of their senses", in *Third Day* of *Two Principal Systems*, quoted by Popper, *loc. cit.*, p. 102.

physicist as to any reflective man – that, once committed to the way of science, he must follow it wherever it leads, even should it lead him straight off his ontological map of reality [1]. It is not surprising that the first response to such a startling revelation is to disassociate the mind from its natural intentionality and to regard the mind as just a clever instrument for the manipulation of nature. A more mature kind of response would lead to the courageous decision to consider – with trepidation – the alternative, namely, the possible revision of the ontological map itself. This is something we shall postpone to another chapter.

This sceptical attitude vis-à-vis the ontological content of scientific theories is shared by many philosophical schools other than those with which scientists are in contact, and for a variety of mutually exclusive reasons [2]. In humanistic and personalist circles, science has always been regarded as an enemy of true culture. This attitude has been described as one for which "science is nothing but glorified plumbing, glorified gadget–making – 'mechanics': very useful but a danger to true culture, threatening us with the dominion of the near-illiterate (of Shakespeare's 'mechanicals')" [3].

Such authors do not always have a profound understanding of science and of the forces motivating and inspiring the scientific enterprise. They have a tendency in common to look upon philosophy as the art of evoking a Weltanschauung more profound, more meaningful in the personal sense than any other – but in ill-concealed rivalry with the pretensions of science to say anything of value about the meaning and intimate structure of nature. The intentionality-structure of the scientist projects a world organised by number and in symbol, and so earns the rebuke of more than one illustrious representative of the philosophical school in question. Hegel, for example, in the *Phenomenology of Spirit*, chastising physics, wrote: "The evidence of this defective way of knowing – an evidence on the strength of which mathematics plumes itself and proudly struts before philosophy – rests solely on the poverty of its purpose and the defectiveness of its material and is on that account of a kind that philosophy must scorn to have anything to do with" [4].

---

[1] Heisenberg echoes this thought: "The exact sciences also start from the assumption that in the end it will always be possible to understand nature, even in every new field of experience, but that we may make no *a priori* assumption about the meaning of the word 'understand'", *Physicist's Conception of Nature*, p. 28.

[2] For example, Hegel, Bergson, Dumery, Ruskin, *et al.*

[3] Popper, *loc. cit.*, p. 102.

[4] G. W. F. Hegel, *The Phenomenology of Spirit*, trans. by J. B. Baillie (London: Allen and Unwin, 1961), p. 102 in Preface.

It may be true that scientists have squandered their credit by a raucous scientism which "avoids philosophic depths or covers them superficially with a self-reassurance springing from the success of science" [1], but to dismiss physical science as a mere *techne* is to be guilty of a surprising neglect of the common root buried in subjectivity from which springs the intentional element in all knowledge, and which as an *intentio intendens* sends sap to all branches of cognitive activity: for the *intentio intendens* animating both science and philosophy is the search for being. We shall return to this in a later chapter.

Summary

In this chapter, we discuss the ontological pre-suppositions expressed in the views of various physicists. We find that they may be divided into two classes: (1) those of *rationalist* tendency, belonging mainly to relativity physics, and (2) those of *empiricist* tendency, belonging mainly to quantum physics. We take Einstein as a type of the former class and Wigner as a type of the second class. We add a short critique of both tendencies.

---

[1] E. Husserl, *Die Krisis der europäischen Wissenschaften und die transzendentale Phänomenologie*, cited by M. Ambacher, in *Méthode de la philosophie de la nature* (P.U.F.: 1961), p. 11.

CHAPTER EIGHT

REALITY IN HEISENBERG'S PHILOSOPHY

SECTION I: THE EARLY HEISENBERG

General Outline

Heisenberg's discovery of quantum mechanics was accompanied, as we have seen, by a great insight which was of the nature of a profound metaphysical conversion; it was the discovery of a new meaning for *reality* which was different from that of Newton, Gauss, Maxwell, Hertz and the grand tradition of classical physics. The sudden swing to the crude empiricism which characterised the early days of complementarity did not last in Heisenberg's case, but changed slowly under the subtle polarising influence of a strong rationalist tendency which was in keeping with his temperament and choice and was encouraged by his mathematical powers. Just as Einstein began his philosophic career under the influence of Hume and Mach to end fifty years later in spiritual companionship with Leibniz and Spinoza, so Heisenberg began as a disciple of Hume and ended in the company of Kant. The transition was not sudden like his first conversion, nor was he conscious of the growing complexity of his thought. If he had been, he would have taken greater pains in his later writings to distinguish his early views from his later. The only indication of the metamorphosis that occurred between 1925 and 1955 is in the change in usage of such words as "objectivity", "causality", "reality", etc., which a careful examination of the context reveals. We have described this metamorphosis elsewhere as the conquering of Hume by Kant; we might also summarise his philosophical development as the result of a dialectic between the Plato of his temperament and choice, and the empiricism forced upon him by the discovery of quantum mechanics and by the environment of Copenhagen.

Heisenberg's Empiricism

In his early papers and lectures on quantum mechanics, Heisenberg insisted that physical quantities were real only when they were actually observed, i.e., when they were instances describable in Euclidean space at a definite time and given in perception [1]. Whatever "lacked intuitive foundation" [2], whatever had no "observational consequences" [3], whatever is "not experimentally verified" [4] is simply excluded from the realm of physical reality.

The new emphasis on human sensibility might, however, be construed in two different ways: either as constitutive of a new meaning (sense or connotation) for the term *reality* or as contributing merely to a new criterion of the real in human knowing without connoting a corresponding change in sense [5]. The distinction is an important one from the point of view of philosophy; for the basic metaphysical orientation of a philosopher's mind is specified by the sense he assigns to the term "reality". In everyday life, we do not generally distinguish between meaning (or intrinsic connotation) and criteria (which, generally, are extrinsic associations); for it is ordinarily sufficient that in daily life our words are correctly applied and correctly understood, and for this purpose the present distinction is not required. It is a distinction however which, even if acknowledged, is rarely given the epistemological importance it merits. Nagel, for example, and other philosophers of science of a positivistic bias seem to think it is just a question of "terminological interest" and "preferred modes of speech"[6]. Its importance is in the classification of ontological views, for it is only with the help of this distinction that a particular opinion can be situated with accuracy within the traditional extremes of rationalism and empiricism.

As Heisenberg was not consciously aware of this distinction his attitude has to be judged by inference from his statements. In his early writings, the real object of physics tended to be identified with observed events described in everyday or classical physical concepts.

[1] "Modern physics is concerned not with the essence and structure of the atom but with observable events and thus places emphasis on the measurement process" wrote Heisenberg in "Kausalgesetz und Quantum Mechanik", *Erkenntnis*, II (1931), pp. 182–183. He goes on to say that it is not the *Beobachtungsobjekt allein* with which physics deals but the *Beobachtungsvorgänge*. Cf. also *Niels Bohr* etc., p. 22.

[2] Heisenberg, *Zeit. f. Physik*, XXXIII (1925), 879; XLIII (1927), 172.

[3] Heisenberg, *Physical Principles* etc., p. 15.

[4] *Ibid.*, p. 1.

[5] *Supra*, chap. I, sect. I; chap. V, sect. I, e.g., p. 85.

[6] E. Nagel's *Structure of Science* (London: 1961), chap. VI.

Since in the realm of quantum mechanics these do not obey causal laws, the real objects of physics cannot be conceptually or rationally expressed – at least not if the quantum system is conceived to move continuously like a body. Conceptual schemes like the concept "atom", he wrote, merely make possible a simple formulation of the laws governing all physical and chemical processes [1]. All this implied a rejection of the classical rationalist thesis. Moreover, in his description of the subject-object relation in which the criterion of the real is found, the type of opposition he describes is clearly conceived to be one of spatial exteriority [2]. Thus, one aspect of Heisenberg's philosophical conversion is correctly described as the discovery of a new and essentially empiricist (or phenomenalist) meaning for *reality*.

Influence of Plato

Heisenberg, however, was not happy in this condition; for both by temperament and by training he inclined to speculative, abstract and formal theories. Even in his early writings, one can find the implicit distinction between two classes of "real objects": the "empirically real" and the "rationally real", which were not, however, distinguished consciously and consciously compared [3]. If empirical reality lacked the properties of formal symmetry, invariance and necessity, then there must be another kind of reality which was the bearer of these; for Heisenberg was deeply imbued with the conviction that rationality (or at least legality) was a universal law, and for him its absence was an unendurable intellectual scandal. In this respect, he was the antithesis of Bohr who, after "muddling through" brilliantly, was ready to conclude that reality is, after all, a "muddle".

If Bohr represented the influence of Protagoras, Heisenberg came early under the spell of Plato. He tells that when he was eighteen years old the abortive communist revolution of 1919 took place in Bavaria. He was temporarily drafted into the army and sent to guard the Theological Seminary in Munich [4]. There he talked philosophy with the students and spent the early morning hours after sunrise on the roof of the seminary reading the *Timaeus* of Plato [5]. He was much impressed by the notion that behind this illusory world of sense, there

[1] Heisenberg, *Philosophic Problems* etc., p. 56.
[2] Heisenberg, *Physical Principles* etc., pp. 58, 64. Also cf. *supra*, pp. 86f.
[3] Cf. Heisenberg, *Philosophic Problems* etc., pp. 20–26, 106–107.
[4] Heisenberg, *Physicist's Conception of Nature*, pp. 53–58.
[5] *Ibid.*, pp. 53–58; *Philosophic Problems* etc., 35, 98; also cf. "Planck's Discovery and the Problems of Modern Physics" by W. Heisenberg in *On Modern Physics* (London: Orion Press, 1961), p. 19.

was a real world of elementary particles which were pure mathematical forms.

The influence of Plato was to lead him to a conviction which he retained throughout even his empiricist days that there were two kinds of realities: intelligible realities which were the objects of *episteme* or intellectual intuition, and sensible objects which were objects of sensible intuition. He believed that we lacked the former kind of knowledge. The combination of abstractive understanding and empirical intuition to which we were reduced in consequence obtained for us merely token or symbolic knowledge of physical reality but not true knowledge. The type of symbolic knowledge characteristic of physical science he called *dianoia*. These early views led him naturally in the direction of Kant [1].

SECTION II: HEISENBERG AND KANT

The Crisis of Kantian Critique

The second great influence on Heisenberg's thought was Kant, and it was within the Kantian problematic that Heisenberg eventually came to find his spiritual home. We have noted how his lively interest in Plato prepared his mind. Kant's transcendental method of philosophy, moreover, makes an unfailing appeal to a theoretical physicist, for its starting point, viz., the acceptance of universal and necessary scientific laws is one towards which he is sympathetically disposed. Because of this peculiar dependence of Kantian philosophy on classical physics, the first serious impact of modern physics on the world of philosophy was its effect on the transcendental critique. Relativity overthrew the absoluteness of Euclidean geometry and quantum mechanics showed that causality in science (in the sense of antecedent-consequent legality between phenomena) was not universal or necessary [2]. If the Kantian starting point is mistaken, if science presupposes no universal or necessary principles then there is no problematic, and the philosophy built upon it – however sublime – is no more than a piece of groundless fancy. This collapse of the most

---

[1] Heisenberg, *Philosophic Problems* etc., pp. 32–34. The distinction between the two classes of objects and their relation to Kant was already expressed in a lecture given in 1934. He adds: "There has not yet been a discussion based upon the new outlook that is sufficiently thorough to show how far this idea [of the *a priori*] is still fruitful in the wider philosophical fields which were essential for Kant", *Philosophic Problems* etc., p. 21.

[2] *Ibid.*, p. 20; *Erkenntnis*, II (1931), pp. 182–183; *On Modern Physics*, p. 12.

prestigious of classical metaphysical schemes was certainly one of the major contributing causes of the practical hegemony of positivism in scientific circles during the years following the discovery of relativity and quantum mechanics.

The most disturbing failure of Kantian epistemology in modern physics was the failure of causality in quantum mechanics: for without causality there is no stable phenomenal object of experience. Another category, *substance*, consequently fails on the quantum level [1]. For causality can be applied only where there is continuity and coherence in the field of experience, where phenomena are grouped into localised wholes which preserve their self-identity in time and move along continuous trajectories in three-dimensional Euclidean space. Causality is then a necessary condition for the application of the category of substance in human experience. "Nature, through the medium of modern physics", wrote Heisenberg, "has reminded us very clearly that we should never hope for such a firm basis [as Cartesian rationalism] for the comprehension of the whole field of 'things perceptible'" [2]. The failure of causality in quantum mechanics meant the breakdown of the attempt to view nature as a systematic totality of related bodies: nature must henceforth be described in terms of individual observation events, i.e., instantaneously localised occurrences – atomic reality-elements, as it were – for which we fashion artificial links through which they are connected "in an abstract space" [3].

Substance, in Kantian epistemology, or the permanent filling of the category of reality, symbolised the presence of noumenal reality, which itself remained, however, shrouded in mystery. The failure of the category of *substance* in quantum mechanics broke the link between the quantum mechanical object and noumenal reality. If a quantum mechanical system is not a stable phenomenal object, i.e., not a "substance", then neither in the Kantian view does it symbolise a noumenal reality.

These thoughts were scarcely more than implicit in Heisenberg's mind for a long time after the discovery of quantum mechanics. During this period he was dominated uneasily by an idealistic (or positivistic) empiricism more in the tradition of Berkeley and Mach than in that of Hume or Locke.

[1] *Erkenntnis, loc. cit.*, pp. 172–182; *Physical Principles* etc., pp. 2, 63. Cf. I. Kant, *Critique of Pure Reason*, trans. by N. Kemp Smith, p. 212 for "substance" and p. 218 for "causality".
[2] *Philosophic Problems* etc., p. 25.
[3] *Ibid.*, p. 93.

SECTION III: THE MATURE HEISENBERG

Abgeschlossene Theorien

There were some physicists, however, and among them Heisenberg, who were unwilling to accept the facile solution of positivistic empiricism and sought a new basis of universality and necessity in science on which to found a transcendental critique. Kant's starting point was mistaken. Was this just a historical accident resulting from the uncritical overconfidence of his epoch in Newtonian science, or was the collapse of universal and necessary laws irremediable? Heisenberg gradually developed a solution over the years which saved the Kantian problematic. Some of the elements of the solution, e.g., the notion of a *closed (abgeschlossene)* theory, were already in his mind as early as 1934 [1], others were suggested by the nature of the research on elementary particles and cosmic rays which he pursued for many years.

A *closed* or *complete (abgeschlossene) theory* is a formal, axiomatisable symbolic system, e.g., a mathematical theory, with a more or less well-defined domain of valid applicability in experience [2]. It represents then a *pure mathematical form* like the triangles and tetrahedrons of the *Timaeus*. Its domain of applicability in experience is usually restricted. Our knowledge of the extent of these limits is always open to revision [3]. However, it represents a form which, once discovered and tested, is "valid for the entire cosmos" and "remains a permanent part of our scientific language and understanding about the world" [4]. The examples he gives are Newtonian mechanics, Maxwell's electromagnetic theory, etc. He rejects the notion that the form of any physical theory is imposed by the mind or by experience; it is, however, "indirectly deduced from experience" [5]. How this comes about he does not say but he seems to suggest that the explanation is partly biological, social

[1] *Naturwissenschaften*, XL (1934), trans. and published in *Philosophic Problems* etc., pp. 11–26.

[2] *Ibid.*, pp. 23–26. 117; for a fuller development of the same theme, see "Abgeschlossene Theorien", *Dialectica*, II (1948), 331–356.

[3] *On Modern Physics*, p. 12.

[4] Heisenberg, *Dialectica, loc. cit.*, p. 335; *Physicist's Conception of Nature*, pp. 27–28 in which he writes that a closed theory is "valid for the entire cosmos and cannot be changed or improved".

[5] Heisenberg, *Zeit. f. Physik*, XLIII (1927), p. 172–198; *Philosophic Problems* etc., p. 23; also *supra*, p. 49.

and historical [1]. Each closed theory is an *a priori* condition of possibility of further theories of more general application, but it is not thereby replaced by the new theory: it remains like the mountain road which leads through a series of scenic prospects to the summit from which the whole can be seen in one, if distant, perspective [2].

Each closed theory possesses a certain degree of necessity and universality but only within its legitimate domain of applicability; none possesses the unrestricted and absolute generality of what Heisenberg calls a *law of nature* [3]. The laws of nature are not relationships between bodies, but general invariances, like the constancy of the velocity of light or of Planck's constant, which govern every physical relationship. Kant, following the physicists of his time, made the mistake of identifying the laws of Euclidean geometry and physical causality with laws of nature; they are not laws of nature but rather *laws of out intuition of nature.*

Heisenberg, who as time went on listened more and more to his Platonic genius, conceived the idea that there was one law of nature which contained all the potentialities of matter. The number of closed theories in present-day physics he reduced to four, viz., Newtonian mechanics, electromagnetic theory (and relativity), the theory of heat, and the quantum theory. The impossibility of uniting them among themselves as they are indicates, he said, the existence of a fifth theory which ties them all together [4]. This he called the *fundamental matter equation.* It would possess all the universal and necessary symmetries of nature. The model for the ascent to more and more universal theories was given by the movement from classical physics to the quantum theory; for not merely was the quantum theory a generalisation of which classical physics was a limiting case, but classical physics remained, in Heisenberg's view, essential to the very definition of quantum physics and *a priori* to its structure [5]. Mounting by steps of greater and greater generality, Heisenberg hoped to reach the submit whence he could hold in the perspective of one universal and necessary equation all known closed theories.

[1] *Dialectica, loc. cit.*, pp. 331–336.
[2] Cf. *Philosophic Problems* etc., p. 76; also W. Heisenberg, *Physics and Philosophy* (New York, *World Perspectives*, vol. 19, Harper 1958), pp. 98–101, 108.
[3] *On Modern Physics*, pp. 5–9; Werner Heisenberg, "Grundlegende Voraussetzungen in der Physik der Elementarteilchen" in *Martin Heidegger zum siebzigsten Geburtstag, 26, ix 59, Festschrift* (Pfullingen: 1959), pp. 291–295.
[4] *Physics and Philosophy*, pp. 98–107, 181–182.
[5] *On Modern Physics*, p. 11.

Universal Equation of Matter

Heisenberg's first attempt was the introduction of the S-Matrix (scattering matrix) in 1943, which he thought had power to yield all observable physical quantities [1]. However, he gave up the search for universality in this direction in favour of a general field-theoretic equation of matter in which the S-Matrix was only a part. This was motivated by his researches into cosmic radiation in which the transmutivity of all particles into energy and of energy into particle-antiparticle pairs was the most striking feature [2]. After Dirac's theory of the positron, it was natural to assume that all such processes depended on a small number of non-linear general equations to explain both the particles and the interactions between them.

From 1950 on Heisenberg devoted his attention increasingly to the programme of constructing a *unified field theory* of matter [3]. The universality of energy as a constituent and determinant of all transmutations led him to suppose that all elementary particles were stationary states of *one physical "matter" system*, just as the different energy levels of the iron atom are stationary states of the "iron atom system" [4]. The universal stuff (Grundstoff) of the "matter" system is *energy;* energy, he says, is the *universal* and *primary substance* like the fire of Heraclitus which keeps everything in motion and of which everything is composed [5].

On many different occasions, Heisenberg asked himself the question: what is the "essence of matter"? [6] He finds exemplified in Greek philosophy two kinds of responses: on the one hand, the *materialism* of Leucippus and Democritus and, on the other hand, the *idealism* of Plato.

He sees in the former the forerunner of classical Cartesian and atomistic materialism which tried to explain material multiplicity by reducing everything to spatially coordinated systems of classical

---

[1] *Zeitschrift f. Physik*, cxx (1943), 513, 673; cxxiii (1944), 93.

[2] E.g., W. Heisenberg, *Vorträge über kosmische Strahlung* (Berlin: 1943) and his many papers published in the *Zeit f. Physik*.

[3] *Zeit. f. Naturforsch.*, 5a (1950), 251, 367; and the summary of these articles in *Comm. Pure and Appl. Math.*, iv (1951), 15–22. The later series of articles comprises the following: *Nachr. d. Gött, Akad. d. Wiss.*, 11a (1953), 111; *Z. f. Naturf.*, 10a (1955), 425; 14a (1959), 441; 16a (1961), 726; For an up-to-date summary of the position of the theory see W. Heisenberg, "Die Entwicklung der einheitlichen Feldtheorie der Elementarteilchen", *Naturwissen.*, L (1963), pp. 3–7.

[4] Heisenberg, *Naturwissen.*, loc. cit., p. 3.

[5] *On Modern Physics*, p. 16; *Physics and Philosophy*, p. 71.

[6] *Philosophic Problems* etc., pp. 51–53, 95–108; *Physicist's Conception of Nature*, pp. 43–46; *On Modern Physics*, pp. 3–20; *Physics and Philosophy*, pp. 61, 166. *Martin Heidegger Festschrift*, pp. 292–297.

elementary particles. According to the principles of atomistic materialism, a classical elementary particle was a body unextended (or
infinitesimal but of fixed dimensions), impenetrable, discontinuous,
internally changeless, homogeneous and permanent in self-identity;
its key properties were indestructibility and indivisibility. Heisenberg
rejects this view; for the attempt to divide an elementary particle in
modern physics may lead either to the destruction of the particle or
paradoxically to the creation of new ones [1]. In order to "divide" a
very small particle, a pulse of very high energy must be used, since the
wave length of the pulse must be smaller than the diameter of the
particle. For any of the elementary particles this energy is sufficient
to enable conversions to take place between radiant energy (photons)
and mass energy (with the "creation" of particles), or between kinetic
energy and mass energy according to Einstein's equation $E = mc^2$ [2].
The resulting "splinters" from a high energy collision are elementary
particles and some of these can be of the same type as the original
particle. Moreover, since particles of the same type are *indistinguishable*
from one another, individual particles of one type have no independent
identity within a shower of like particles. The "splinters" are actually
not splinters of the original particle but merely a new way or "channel"
of partitioning the total energy brought together by the collision.
Energy seems to play the role of a common *"universal substance"* or
"universal matter". Under these circumstances, classical "indestructibility" and "indivisibility" lose their significance. The dominant
ideas in the new physics are those of *"particle or system creation"* and
"particle or system annihilation", under conditions where the form of
energy is changed. Because of these reasons, Heisenberg rejected the
materialism of Leucippus and Democritus.

It should be remarked that when Heisenberg uses the term materialism", as he does of every intentionality-structure which anticipates a
mechanistic (reductionist or atomistic) explanation of nature, he does
not use it in the strong philosophical sense of a materialism which
denies the existence of a spiritual order intrinsically independent of
matter. He is thinking principally of scientific theories of nature.

Moreover, he wrongly assumes that *dialectical materialism* is a
mechanistic materialism; it is deterministic, but not necessarily
mechanistic. In his criticism of Soviet "materialist ontology", his most
fundamental objection seems to be to the claim of *realism* that it

---

[1] *Philosophic Problems* etc., pp. 95–108.
[2] *On Modern Physics*, p. 15; *Physics and Philosophy*, p. 73.

makes; that is, to its assertion that the quantum theory is *objectively valid* – valid, that is, about physical situations which do not necessarily include conscious acts of observation of some physicist [1]. For example, according to Blokhintsev, the objective situation described by quantum physics is a virtual collectivity of microsystems in a perturbing environment. For Alexandrov, it is an individual microscopic system with really determinate properties which, however, are only potential vis-à-vis measurement [2]. Heisenberg's fundamental objection to these views is that they treat the observer-instrument (or environment) as separable from the observer-scientist (as a conscious agent). Heisenberg declares that such a separation is impossible and because of this an *idealistic interpretation* of the quantum theory is imposed by the theory itself.

We have shown that this view stems from a parallelistic theory of knowledge which is uncritically presupposed and which we believe is not an acceptable philosophical theory [3]. Heisenberg's *idealism*, like the *dialectical materialism* of Blokhintsev, Alexandrov and Omel'-yanovsky, follows from a pre-conceived intentionality structure which, by anticipating the forms of scientific theories, inserts them into a philosophical context even before they are born.

Heisenberg rejected the materialism of Leucippus and Democritus and his choice fell on Plato: "The World", he wrote, "is the image of an idea, viz., a mathematical symmetry" [4]. One thinks of the geometrical figures with which Plato identified the elementary particles. In place of the geometrical figures Heisenberg substitutes the eigen solutions of a *universal matter equation*. These are intelligible (and mathematical) objects like the figures of the *Timaeus;* but, he says, they have a dual structure different from Plato's forms and which he claims is parallel to the Aristotelian hylomorphic conception [5]. The "universal substance" or "universal" or "primary matter" is *energy:*

---

[1] *Niels Bohr* etc., pp. 21–23, which is substantially the same as "Die Entwicklung der Deutung der Quantentheorie", *Physikalische Blätter*, XII (1956), pp. 289–304, espec. p. 294.

[2] D. I. Blokhintsev, *Grundlagen der Quantenmechanik* (Berlin: 1953), pp. 498–499, and "Kritika filosofskikh vozzreny tak nazyvaemoy Kopenhagenskoy shkoly v fizike" (Critique of the philosophical viewpoint of the so-called 'Copenhagen School')", in *Filosofskie voprosy sovremennoy fizike* (Philosophical Problems of Modern Physics) Moskow: 1952), pp. 358–395. A. D. Alexandrov, *Dokl. Akad. Nauk.*, LXXXIV (1952). The philosophical doctrine of Soviet physicists is admirably summarised by G. Wetter, S.J., in *Dialectical Materialism*, trans. from the German by P. Heath (London: Routledge and Kegan Paul, 1958), pp. 405–416.

[3] *Supra*, chap. IV, pp. 57–80.

[4] *On Modern Physics*, pp. 5–6; cf. also *Philosophic Problems* etc., pp. 73, 86–87.

[5] Hylomorphism states that the essence of a material being is composed of two inseparable principles of being – (primary) matter and (substantial) form.

the form is a *mathematical eigen state function* [1]. Aristotelian universal (or primary) matter is the principle of dispersion, diversity and multiplicity and hence of unintelligibility. Heisenberg's *universal matter*, which he identifies with energy, is, on the contrary, merely a part of a compound intelligible whole, for energy is an intelligible principle associated with certain invariance properties of a system relative to a manifold of space-time frames of reference. Once again we have evidence of the basic rationalism of Heisenberg's thought.

As for the distinction between "elementary" and "non-elementary" Heisenberg says that the distinction has no longer any validity or utility. Each form, whatever its atomic (baryon) number or charge, is a unique excitation of the basic matter energy field and may be considered elementary [2]. A physical system is *elementary* if all its free physical states can be obtained by kinematic transformations belonging to the inhomogeneous Lorentz group from a single basic state. The definition unfortunately does not rule out a bound system like the deuteron which has only a single bound state. If one attempts to define the notion of *particle* as an elementary system which is perfectly localizable (that is, which occupies at any instant a virtually unextended point) then one meets insuperable difficulties in relativistic quantum physics. A relativistic particle cannot be defined unequivocally by place. Wigner and Newton came to the weak conclusion that an elementary particle is an elementary system which it is *useful* to regard as *structureless* [3]. The failure of the materialistic notion of exact localizability adds point to Heisenberg's rejection of it.

One of the most general laws of nature, Heizenberg surmised, was the existence of a natural unit of length of magnitude approximately 10^{-13} cm. The existence in physics of only two fundamental physical constants, viz., the velocity of light (c) and Planck's constant (h), leaves an arbitrariness in the unit of length (and a corresponding arbitrariness in the unit of mass) which is a lack of symmetry and suggests the existence of a natural standard of length [4]: for example, the ultra-violet divergence of quantum field theory and the problem of vacuum fluctuations and pair production when attempts are made

---

[1] *Physics and Philosophy*, p. 63; *Naturwissen., loc. cit.*, pp. 3–7.

[2] *Philosophic Problems* etc., p. 57.

[3] T. D. Newton and E. P. Wigner, *Rev. Mod. Physics*, XXI (1949), 400.

[4] First suggested by Heisenberg in *Zeit. f. Physik*, CX (1938), 251–266 and developed in *Ann. d. Physik*, XXXII (1938), 20–33. Cf. also W. Heisenberg, "Wahrscheinlichkeitsaussagen in der Quantentheorie der Wellenfelder", *Actualités scientifiques et industrielles*, no. 734 (Paris: 1938), pp. 44–51.

to measure lengths smaller than 10^{-13} cm [1]. As early as 1938, he had suggested a new universal constant of the dimension of length as a solution of the renormalization problem in quantum field theory [2]. In his unified theory of elementary particles, of which the first paper appeared in 1950, he showed how such a constant could be incorporated naturally into the universal matter-energy equation [3].

Natural Symmetries

It does not help our purpose to enter into the mathematical form of the different equations suggested and studied by Heisenberg. We are interested principally in the intentionality-structure of his thought and the epistemological consequences he intended to draw. In his opinion, the important characteristics of the universal equation are its *symmetries*, i.e., the number and kinds of transformation groups under which it retains its mathematical form. The physical structure of space-time is expressed by the invariance of all equations under the inhomogeneous Lorentz (or Poincaré) group [4]. The invariants of this group are *mass* and *spin*. The *creation operator* of a physical system must be a representation of the Lorentz group characterised by the mass and spin of the system. Other field symmetries yield the other properties which characterise the elementary particle: for example, certain gauge transformation invariances yield *electric charge, baryon* and *lepton number*, while *strangeness* is a property associated with transformations in isotopic spin space. In many elementary particle field theories a minimum number of independent fields (e.g., a baryon field, a lepton field, etc.) carry the symmetries characteristic of the elementary particles. Heisenberg, however, has tried to generate all the elementary particles out of one basic non-linear unified field [5]. In this he has not so far been successful.

The importance of his research, however, from the philosophical point of view lies in the intention (or intentionality-structure) animating this pursuit; for the intention specifies a horizon towards which it looks and in which is sketched an anticipation of the reality to be discovered. The idea which dominates Heisenberg's thinking to-day is that of *symmetry relations*, which he holds constitute the essential

---

[1] *Actualités scientifiques* etc., *loc. cit.*, pp. 49–50; *On Modern Physics*, p. 15. The same idea was put forward at the same time by P. A. M. Dirac in *Nature*, CXXXIX (1937), p. 323 and *Proc. Roy. Soc., A.*, CLXV (1938), p. 199.

[2] *Zeit. f. Physik*, CX (1938), 251–266.

[3] Cf. note 3, p. 144.

[4] *Infra*, chap. X, pp. 172–174.

[5] Cf. note 3, p. 144.

expression of a law of nature. In this respect he represents a direction of physical research which was introduced into quantum physics by Weyl and Wigner and which has recently been applied to the multiplicity of elementary particles by Gell-Mann, Y Ne'eman, Salam and others with striking success. The validity of symmetry hypotheses in physics has received dramatic confirmation resently in the prediction and subsequent discovery of the Omega-minus hyperon [1].

With the change in his philosophical orientation, the content of *complementarity* has also undergone for Heisenberg a subtle change. Gone is the positivist emphasis of the early days, and the central place is now occupied by the *symmetry* of wave and particle representations. For him to-day the essence of complementarity is this symmetry, and, because symmetries are sacred, complementarity also has a sacred quality [2]. In the volume *Niels Bohr and the Development of Physics* (1955), in which he answers the opponents of the Copenhagen interpretation, his principal argument against all those who favour a unitary (particle or field) interpretation is that they abandon a basic symmetry of physical knowledge, viz., the complementarity of wave and particle representations which he believes expresses a universal law of our knowing and an essential aspect of physical theory. He ends his examination thus: "Since all counter-proposals hitherto made against the Copenhagen interpretation have found themselves compelled to sacrifice essential symmetry properties of the quantum theory, we may well suppose that the Copenhagen interpretation is unavoidable if these symmetry properties, like the Lorentz invariance, are held to be a genuine feature of Nature" [3]. For our own part, we would like to point out that, while Lorentz invariance is a physical law, the symmetry of wave and particle postulated by the principle of complementarity is not a physical law but a way of interpreting physics from the point of view of a certain theory of knowledge.

Objectivity

The preponderating importance which symmetry relations now have for Heisenberg indicates the predominantly rationalist character of his present-day thinking. This is also reflected in the gradual shift in the connotation of the term "objectivity" from a predominantly

[1] Cf. *infra*, chap. x, note 2, p. 175.
[2] *Niels Bohr* etc., pp. 12–29; *Physics and Philosophy*, p. 44–58.
[3] *Niels Bohr* etc., p. 28.

empiricist to a predominantly rationalist sense [1] – that is from the sense of *objectivity* used of an empirically given object to that used of a general and abstract conceptual content. In Heisenberg's early writings, objective knowledge referred to the *phenomenal objectivity* of an observed event [2]: in his later writings, however, "objective" almost always means "independent of the circumstances under which a statement is verified", i.e., the *public objectivity of a concept* [3]. He eventually came to contrast "objective" with "real" or "actual" (*"wirklich"*). A wave function, he says, is "objective but not real"[4]; for *real* or *actual* implies an empirical content while *objective* does not [5]. The logical consequence, from which Heisenberg does not shy, is that quantum mechanics is a science of immanent acts and objects; it no longer "describes nature but our knowledge of nature", as he wrote [6]. This raised acutely the problem of how the objective features of quantum mechanics were related to noumenal reality. In everyday life and in classical physics, a stable phenomenal object (implying an application of the Kantian category of *substance*) mediates symbolically between the subject and the noumenal reality; in quantum mechanics, however, there is no such symbol of an independent external reality. How then can quantum mechanics escape the circle of immanence? Or does it? [7].

Aristotelian "Potentia"

Heisenberg came eventually to consider this problem and around 1955 he proposed a solution which illustrates very well the meaning he now gives to the subjectivity inherent in quantum mechanics. An objective description of a quantum mechanical system referring to three-dimensional space, like the description of an elementary particle or an atom, he called a *dunamis* or *potentia* or an *objective tendency*

---

[1] There is also a corresponding shift in the connotation of the term "causality", from *phenomenal causality* (v.g., *Physical Principles* etc., pp. 2, 63; *Erkenntnis, loc. cit.*, pp. 172–182) to a more abstract *rational* causality (*Martin Heidegger Festschrift*, p. 295).

[2] Cf. *Philosophic Problems* etc., pp. 20, 45, 86–87, 92; for example, he writes: "We can only communicate the course and result of a measurement by describing the necessary manual actions and instrumental readings as objective, as events taking place in the space and time of our *Anschauung*", p. 20.

[3] *Niels Bohr* etc., pp. 25–26; *Physics and Philosophy*, pp. 53, 81, 133; *Physicist's Conception of Nature*, p. 24.

[4] *Niels Bohr* etc., p. 27.

[5] *Ibid.*, p. 27; *Physics and Philosophy*, p. 130.

[6] *Physicist's Conception of Nature*, pp. 25; cf. also pp. 15, 29–31.

[7] Heisenberg states the problem dramatically: "For the first time in the course of history, man on this earth now confronts himself alone", *Physicist's Conception of Nature*, p. 23.

borrowing the terms and the idea, as he believed, from Aristotle [1]. On the one hand, the elementary particle is not phenomenally real; for it has "no colour, no smell, no taste; . . . and the concepts of geometry and kinematics, like shape or motion in space, cannot be applied to it consistently [2]. On the other hand, it is not a pure *(inhaltsleer)* idea, for it can be "converted from potency to act" by the process of measurement and observation. Heisenberg called it *real but potential* [3]. The wave packet of an elementary particle (or its probability wave) is a "quantitative formulation of the concept of *dunamis*. . . in Aristotle's philosophy", he wrote [4].

This is a thing-in-itself kind of reality, and hence noumenal; but it is not conceived to be opposed by exteriority to the subject and hence, in Heisenberg's view, it is not just another kind of external reality independent of a knowing subject. It is the noumenal condition of possibility of the wave packet (or objective tendency) which accounts for the distribution of possible observable events linked by the wave packet. The actualization of an event by observation, however, results from a more or less confused union of subject and object. The objective tendency or *potentia* then is the *noumenal correlate of this union of subject and object* in experience. It is then on the one hand *not* simply the thing-in-itself in the external world, *nor* on the other hand is it simply the transcendental ego; it bridges both the external world and the transcendental subjectivity of the knower. As Heisenberg wrote in the *Martin Heidegger Festschrift* (1959), "the search for the natural laws of the [ultimate structure of matter,] entails the use of general principles of which it is not clear whether they apply to the empirical behaviour of the world or to *a priori* forms of our thought, or to the way in which we speak" [5].

It is in this light that passages like the following have to be read: "The objective reality of the elementary particle has been dispersed, not into the fog of some ill-defined or still unexplained conception of reality, but into the transparent clarity of a mathematics that no longer describes the behaviour of the elementary particles but only our

---

[1] *Niels Bohr* etc., p. 13; *Physics and Philosophy*, pp. 41, 53, 70, 91, 180, 185; *On Modern Physics*, p. 9.

[2] *Physics and Philosophy*, p. 70.

[3] "In the experiments about atomic events we have to do with things and facts with phenomena that are just as real as any phenomena of daily life. But the atoms or elementary particles themselves are not as real: they form a world of potentialities and possibilities rather than one of things and facts", *Physics and Philosophy*, p. 186. Cf. also *On Modern Physics*, p. 13.

[4] *On Modern Physics*, p. 9.

[5] *Martin Heidegger Festschrift*, p. 291.

knowledge of this behaviour. The atomic physicist has had to resign himself to the fact that his science is but a link in the infinite chain of man's argument with nature and that it cannot simply speak of nature 'in itself'" [1].

It should be noted that, while the philosophic setting of Heisenberg's thought is so entirely foreign to that of Aristotle that it is scarcely worth while to compare them, there does exist an analogy between Heisenberg's use of *dunamis* (or *potentia* or potency) and the two principal usages made by Aristotle of this word and of the related *dunathon*. The first is that of *passive potency* or the simultaneous possibility of contradictories; as, for instance, in Aristotle's example, the simultaneous possibility of sickness and health [2]. In this sense, Heisenberg's usage would correspond to the possibility in the subject of experiencing (or observing) one of a variety of possibilities linked by the wave function; it connotes the contingency of actual observation events. The second sense is that of *active potency* or the power to impress a form on some matter in the measure of the disposition of the matter to receive this form [3]; this would be analogous to Heisenberg's noumenal correlate as somehow related actively to the impression received in observation. The analogy, however, cannot be pushed too far.

SECTION IV: HEISENBERG'S "PRACTICAL REALISM"

In conclusion, we shall summarise briefly what we believe to be Heisenberg's general philosophic position vis-à-vis the three authors with whom he considers himself in dialogue, and who span his thought like three axes of reference: namely, Kant, Plato and Aristotle. He has given his own philosophic position the name *Practical Realism* [4].

Heisenberg and Kant

The most pervasive characteristic of Heisenberg's thought and that which indicates his spiritual home is without doubt the Kantian critique. Like Kant, his starting point is the existence of universal and necessary laws of nature, and the problematic he envisages is

---

[1] *Physicist's Conception of Nature*, p. 15.

[2] *Phys.* III, 201 a, 34. Cf. A. Mansion, *Introduction à la Physique Aristotélicienne* (Louvain: 1945), p. 284.

[3] *Metaph.*, IX, 2, 1046 b 2–4. Cf. Mansion, *loc. cit.*, pp. 114, 230.

[4] *Physics and Philosophy*, pp. 81–83.

entirely circumscribed by the Kantian question concerning the conditions of possibility of such science.

Heisenberg, however, was faced with a double problem: the establishing of a valid starting point in science for the transcendental critique and the solution of the new kind of problem set by the peculiar properties of the quantum mechanical system.

His answer to the problem of a starting point was in the distinction between, on the one hand, laws of nature which are universal and necessary aspects of all scientific objects, and, on the other hand, two sets of laws of restricted generality, laws between objects and laws of our intuition of nature. Kant had made the mistake of taking the laws of our intuition of nature (i.e., everyday experience organised by the concepts of classical physics) to be universal and necessary laws of nature. They are not; nor are laws governing certain classes of objects laws of nature. Now, no law of restricted generality or contingent in its application is capable of creating the typical problematic of transcendental philosophy. Are there such universal and necessary laws which all scientific objects obey? In its first impact, quantum mechanics tended to cast doubt on the existence of any such laws of nature. However, a law like the constancy of the velocity of light which is the result of a universal symmetry with respect to a class of space-time transformations is an example which quantum mechanics has not overthrown. Heisenberg has devoted himself in recent years to discovering what he believes to exist, namely, one law of nature which sums up all the necessary and universal symmetries of matter; this he calls the fundamental "matter" equation of the unified field. The science of the fundamental "matter" equation takes on for Heisenberg something of the importance of the Pure Science of Nature for Kant.

The second problem concerned the crisis provoked by the failure of causality for objects of quantum mechanics. These turned out to be objects to which the category of "substance" does not validly apply. Heisenberg concluded that the true object of quantum mechanics was not nature but "man's relationships with nature" [1], i.e., the subject-object union occuring in the act of observation. As a consequence, a new kind of noumenal reality in which subject and object cannot be separated from one another, he called *dunamis* or *potentia* or *objective tendency*.

---

[1] *Physicist's Conception of Nature*, p. 29.

Heisenberg and Plato

Heisenberg has always considered himself to be a disciple of the Plato of the *Timaeus*. Behind the changing and illusory appearances of the sensible world, there are the real and unchanging mathematical forms. Like Plato, however, and Kant, Heisenberg never overcame the duality of two objects of knowledge: objects of sensibility and objects of understanding. The historical evolution of his ontology was the gradual shift from objects of sensible intuition as defining the content of the term "reality" (his empiricist phase) to those of intellectual intuition *(episteme)*. Abstractive understanding *(dianoia)* became for him a complicated criterion or symbol of noumenal reality rather than an expression of it (his mature phase). However, the multiplicity of objects remains for Heisenberg unharmonised and is the principal source of inconsistency in his utterances.

Heisenberg and Aristotle

Heisenberg borrowed two ideas (or terms) from Aristotle: the notion of *dunamis* (or potency) and *hylomorphism*, or the theory that sensible reality is composed of a formal principle (which for him was a mathematical form) and a material principle (which for him was energy as a *universal substance*). In the case of *dunamis* (or potency), we have pointed out that this refers to a noumenal structure constituted by the union of subject and object in the act of observation – and not a reality which is objective in the sense of being independent of whether or not it is an object of knowledge. Similarly the reality which is composed of two hylomorphic principles is not simply what we think of as the external world, but the mutual presence of (knowing) subject and (known) object when they interact. Moreover, Heisenberg's *universal* or *primary matter* (or *substance*) is essentially different from Aristotle's passive principle of multiplicity (which is also the universal subject of all material change): as far as we can judge, it is merely a part of a compound intelligible form.

Summary

This chapter contains a study of Heisenberg's views of the ontological content of quantum mechanics from 1925 until the present day. During the quantum revolution of 1925, he began by accepting a Berkeley-type empiricism in which the reality of a quantum mechanical system was reduced to that of a set of observation events, which were, however, acausally connected and in consequence did not constitute a stable phenomenal object of experimental knowledge. After 1955, he professed a modified form of Kantian philosophy whose starting point was the existence of universal and necessary scientific laws. Those universal and necessary scientific laws from which Kant started have been shown to belong only to restricted domains of intuitive experience (the domain of everyday life and classical physics). Heisenberg defines noumenal reality as the object of an intellectual intuition (episteme) which, however, is a kind of knowledge we do not possess. We know noumenal reality only through symbols in an intellectually patterned experience. There are two kinds of noumenal reality: there is the thing-in-itself which is the correlate of the phenomenal object, and there is the *dunamis* (or Aristotelian *potentia* or objective tendency) which is the correlate of the quantum mechanical system (e.g., elementary particle, atom, etc.). The latter is the noumenal correlate of the phenomenal or experienced union of subject and object taking place in the act of observation. The importance of universal symmetries in the expression of general laws of nature is stressed by Heisenberg, and these constitute for him the true basis for transcendental philosophy.

CHAPTER NINE

ONTOLOGICAL STRUCTURE OF PHYSICAL REALITY

SECTION I: JUSTIFICATION OF REALISM IN PHYSICAL SCIENCE

"Reality" and Human Polymorphic Consciousness

If there is one conclusion which imposes itself before all others as a result of the inquiry we have made, it is the ambiguity hidden in the sense of the term "physical reality". This is founded in turn upon the underlying polymorphism of the human way of knowing reality. The neglect of some elements of this polymorphic consciousness, or undue emphasis on certain aspects of it are the roots from which spring a multiplicity of epistemological difficulties; for in every question there is a hidden structure directing implicitly the search for answers, and prior even to the formulation of the answer and imposing a structure upon the answer even before it is formulated. This hidden structure is the domain of intentionality and, like the nine-tenths of an iceberg below water, it lies perilously below the level of our cognitive activities. Because of failure to appreciate this, many ontological and epistemological discussions, especially wherever positivism or linguistic analysis is dominant, tend to founder; for, in such cases, problems are generally formulated uniquely in the light of the one-tenth that is in public view.

By saying that the human way of knowing is polymorphic, we mean that it is a composite act in which many different activities take part in subordinated roles. Three activities are particularly prominent in such an act; viz., empirical intuition, conceptual understanding and rational affirmation (or judgement). Still it is one act and not many acts; since its purpose is to express a single, if composite, object of knowledge. However, the polymorphism of human consciousness creates many problems. Some of its elements, for instance, may be overlooked. Or alternatively, the diversity of its activities may be recognised but divided into two classes: one constituting the class which really knows *reality* and which can be used to define the sense of the term "reality" (since reality is, by supposition, its object), and a second class which is considered inessential to this knowledge either because it constitutes merely a provisional or imperfect stage of knowledge or because it provides us merely with criteria of reality which are subjective and extrinsic to the essential definition of reality. We have had occasion to describe the two extremes of simplification: *empiricism* which tends to devaluate conceptual knowledge and to emphasise the act of empirical intuition, as the essential cognitive act defining (for us) the sense of the term "reality", and *rationalism* which tends to devaluate empirical knowledge and to see the mind's essential function as that of defining conceptually the essences of real things.

We admit both types of knowledge as essential to the expression of concrete physical reality and by so doing place ourselves within the perspective of the *abstractionist theory of knowledge* outlined in Chapter One. That is, we hold that conceptual understanding is not itself alone an adequate expression of concrete physical reality; but that its function is to yield an ideal relational norm compared with which individual cases depart only randomly. The function of recognising individual cases is performed by empirical intuition. It follows from this, as we have shown, that the most complete knowledge we can have of a physical system is the combination of a deterministic theory (specifying the ideal norm) and a statistical theory (specifying the ideal frequencies of departures from the norm within a random sample of individual cases).

Heisenberg's Ontology Criticised

Heisenberg, after an initial phase of empiricism, rediscovered the ontological value of rational thought. The discovery was made however under the influence of Plato from whom the dual objects of knowledge, objects of sensibility and objects of understanding were strongly contrasted and opposed. The influence of Kant caused him to admit: yet a third class of possible objects, namely, noumenal objects. So much cognitional wealth was a mixed blessing for it created the problem of harmonising the diverse elements and of stating their relation to one another and their ontological value. The problem for Heisenberg was rendered practically insoluble by reason of an implicit supposition that the three objects of knowledge were three fully constituted, if linked, objects, and not three aspects entering into the constitution of one object. Within the Kantian problematic as Heisenberg understood it, "reality", as the aim and objective of our knowing powers, tended to have a triple degeneracy which could be resolved in different ways: by the simple process of suppressing one or other element in the degeneracy, or by the reversal of all three in favour of the exclusive rights of the self-conscious subject to be called real.

"Reality": a Complex Notion

Our own solution is to retain all the elements of the problem but not as a trio of fully constituted objects; rather as revealing complementary aspects of the strict object. The sense in which we use the term *strict object* has already been explained [1]. We shall now review the different functions performed by the three partial aspects (or partial objects) of human knowledge within the whole.

Sensibility

The empirical data received in sensibility serves the twofold function of making present the existence of the reality to be affirmed, recognised or understood (its *presentative* function), and of being a symbol (or part of one) of the nature of the reality presented in and through it (its *representative* function).

In its *presentative function*, sensibility is related to the judgement of existence and is connected with the criterion for us of the affirmation of existence. For example, we can only affirm that a hydrogen atom is in this piece of material if we have some sensible and unambiguous indication of its presence, i.e., an observable symbol of its presence. In the case of the hydrogen atom, this may be a certain spectrum, a certain atomic number, the ability to take part in certain chemical reactions, etc.

In its *representative function*, empirical intuition forms an essential part in the constitution of the observable symbol. The object, in the strict sense, with which we have identified the sense of the term "reality" is that which is symbolised by the observable symbol. It follows from this that there is an aspect of physical reality to which sensibility corresponds and that this aspect is not extrinsic to the ontological constitution of physical reality. Observed data in physics serve to represent individual systems: therefore, the representative function of sensibility is to represent the individuality of concrete cases [2].

---

[1] *Supra*, chap. I, pp. 6–8.

[2] The essential reference to sensibility introduces into the meaning of "reality" the *temporality* which many modern philosophers give as the meaning of "existence". Cf. A. Dondeyne, *La différence ontologique chez M. Heidegger*, p. 24.

Observed data, however, always exhibit an unsystematic aspect with respect to the general law (or ideal norm) to which they more or less conform. The element of randomness in observed data with respect to a general law must also have its representative value. The element of randomness is not merely an expression of human ignorance but an expression of the essential and characteristic structure of human knowing. We argue that there must be an ontological foundation in physical reality which enables it to be known and truly represented by a strict object possessing the structure in question. The ontological foundation must be composite, with a formal or systematic principle or *form* to explain the systematic normative structure of the physical law, and a principle which we call *irreducible matter* to explain the openness and multiplicity of the kind of physical system in question.

Conceptual Understanding

The rational conceptual part serves to add to the data presented in empirical intuition (or to recognise in them) a structure of relations and terms (i.e., a system of *primary relativities*) and an *ideal norm* to which the actual structures conform more or less (this is the *secondary determination of the above*). Consider, for example, Galileo's experiments on projectiles [1]. He surmised that a parabolic relation existed between the vertical distances traversed and the time of flight: the primary structure here is one constituted by a mathematical functional with parameters to be determined. The secondary determination in this case is the explicit value of the constant parameters. The secondary determinations can be crude and inexact and subject to indefinite improvement by improved techniques of measurement. This does not falsify, however, the primary relativities.

The relational structure in question may be of two kinds. It may involve relations between things and things, or it may involve relations between things and certain aspects of sensible experience or utility to a human subject. In both cases, the effect of conceptual analysis is, firstly, to express or to suppose a set of terms and the primary relativities between them, and, secondly, to make precise the ideal normative inter-relation of this set with a view to achieving clarity and precision, e.g., by evaluating the secondary determinations. In physics, precision is obtained by measuring more and more accurately the unknown parameters of the equation.

---

[1] Galileo Galilei, *Dialogues Concerning Two New Sciences* trans. by H. Crew (London: Macmillan, 1914), the "Fourth Day".

We distinguish two classes of such structures: one which constitutes a thing-for-us or property-for-us, and the other which constitutes a thing-for-things or property-for-things [1]. In the first case, since the content of a concept is precisely to relate things or properties to a human subject, it may well be thought that such a concept does not express what a thing is, but merely how it appears to me or how usefully I can employ it. So speaks the instrumentalist philosopher. The reasons he gives would hold if the relations through which we expressed our knowledge of physical reality were merely extrinsic relations, that is, relations founded upon a ground extrinsic to the nature of the related term; as for example, when we speak of a distant object, *distance* is extrinsic to the object considered. However, conceptual knowledge usually prescinds from extrinsic relations in order to construct concepts based upon the activities of things whether to form impressions on human sensibility, to fulfil human desires or to effect changes in the world. Such relations are founded upon what things do, and hence upon what things are: they are *intrinsic relations*. They reveal, in consequence, something of what things are. In the class of things-for-us or properties-for-us, however, the concept is specified by the value (in experience or in action) of the thing or property for us. The thing or property is known only as the term of a select set of relations, whether to the structure of our senses or to the actual human needs and desires to which things respond and which are characteristic of a certain historical situation.

To complement the selectivity of thing-for-us or property-for-us, natural science enters to study the relationships between things themselves. Essential to this study is the use of symbolic (mathematical) formalisms to express closed groups of relations defining one another mutually by implicit definition. Essential to this study also is the use of observable symbols in experience; both as criteria for the judgement of existence and as tokens of the formal effect of particular interactions. In the latter sense, the token can be mapped on the number-system and thereby incorporated into the mathematical formulism which with the rules of correspondence defines the properties-for-things. Since the relations so defined are all based upon interactivity between things these relations are all intrinsic to the structure of physical reality and reveal something about its essence. In general relativity even space and time become intrinsic properties of physical systems [2].

---

[1] *Supra*, chap. IV, pp. 58–68.
[2] *Infra* chap. X, pp. 172–174.

We know physical reality, then, to the extent of its participation in a world of actually interacting things and subjects. We know it, however, only through sensible and intelligible symbols. Does our knowledge go beyond the symbol to reach out even to that which is symbolised? Or does it stop short, as in Heisenberg's explanations, at the symbol leaving the thing-in-itself shrouded in mystery?

Rational Affirmation

This brings us to the sense of the third activity constitutive of the strict object of human knowledge, viz., the act of affirmation (or judgement). What is experienced and what is conceived are only partial and preliminary activities leading – after the weighing of appropriate evidence – to the culmination of a virtually unconditioned affirmation "This is so" [1]. *What is so*, however, is not just a phenomenal object nor a symbol in its material reality, but what the phenomenal object *represents* and what the symbol *symbolises*. Thus, the mind turns about the pivot of the observable symbol and the orgaisation of such sumbols through a mathematical theory, to affirm that which so presents itself in experience, viz., the thing as transcendent to experience and thought and existing independently of whether it is experienced or thought about [2]. This follows from the fact that the concepts of physical science are not things-for-us or properties-for-us, but relationships between things; hence the sense of the affirmation "This is so" expresses what is, whether or not it is experienced or thought.

One might object that even though this be the sense of the affirmation, it could be mistaken – even mistaken as a rule. How do we know that the affirmation does not make its own strict object by setting off its own conception on its own authority against a horizon of absoluteness which is no more than the projection of an ideal and immanent regulative principle governing all human affirmations? While we do not wish to enter here into a lengthy discussion of the critical problem, a few brief points might help to show where we, at least, stand.

[1] In other words we identify the meaning of "physical reality" with that of "existing thing". However, *existence* is not a mere predicate: its sense is expressed by the strong sense of the verb *to be*. We are critical however of some of the implications of G. Maxwell's formula: "Φ_s are real $=_{def} \Phi_s$ exist". This seems to us to imply that the valid application of the term *existence* is limited to *things*, thereby excluding *spirit* as a possible subject of existence. If *existence* in the above formula is restricted to *physical existence* then we should be in entire agreement with the formula. The reference is to "The Ontological Status of Theoretical Entities" by Grover Maxwell, *Minnesota Studies in the Philosophy of Science*, III, p. 21. Cf. also note 2 below.

[2] Cf. Joseph de Finance, *Être et Agir* (Rome: Univ. Greg., 1960), chap. III.

First of all, a universal scepticism about the realistic value of human affirmations is untenable; for, as Augustine saw, to doubt means *really* to doubt and not to doubt one's doubting; hence universal scepticism is self-contradictory. If universal scepticism is self-contradictory, then there exist criteria according to which affirmations may be judged to be well and correctly made or badly and incorrectly made. The sense of the affirmation, however, whether it is well-made (and hence true) or badly made (and hence false) remains the same, viz., to assert *what is* independently of whether or not it is an object of my thought or experience. The criteria for correctly making affirmations is the weighing of evidence. This evidence is often encountered in haphazard fashion in everyday life. In scientific research, however, the business of the scientist is to produce evidence in a systematic fashion, reconnoitring the terrain of a scientific theory strategically, occupying well chosen and strategic points with a view to undisputed mastery of the terrain. No one knows better what this means in any particular field than the trained scientist. The scientific method of experimental testing and verification is the search for and the application of criteria for the correct making of scientific affirmations; but the sense of the scientific affirmation whose justification is sought through these procedures is incurably *realistic*, that is, it intends being as its object [1].

In conclusion, it may be said that if any scientific affirmation is well and correctly made, then it asserts *what truly is*. It may, however take a great deal of difficult and subtle analysis to disengage the physiognomy of the strict object which is affirmed from the matrix of scientific methodology within which it makes its appearance. In our opinion, the real source of epistemological difficulties in the interpretation of quantum mechanics lies here, rather than in disputes about the sense of the act of affirmation or judgement in human knowledge.

SECTION II: ONTOLOGICAL STRUCTURE OF ATOMIC REALITY

Whole and Part of an Atomic System

In what sense are the constitutive parts of a bound many-particle system present in the system? Or in the concrete, in what sense are the proton and the electron present in the hydrogen atom? Is the hydrogen atom merely a compound, perhaps a mechanistic compound, of a proton

---

[1] Cf. B. Lonergan, *Insight*, chapters XI–XIII where the questions discussed in this section are very fully treated.

and an electron? Heisenberg's opinion which we have already reviewed is that there is no essential difference between an elementary and a compound atomic system [1]. That which imposes unity on a system, he says, is a mathematical form and the mathematical form of a hydrogen atom is not just the juxtaposition of two forms, but the excitation of a two-particle (proton and electron) bound state in a fundamental matter (or energy) field. We agree with Heisenberg's conclusion, although we do not concur with the immanentist interpretation he has given to it.

We can reach a similar conclusion by another route. If the proton were an actual physical reality within the atom, then, it should be able to manifest its presence through characteristic types of inter-actions with neighbouring systems. The neighbouring systems would thereby serve the function of a measuring apparatus: the character-istic effects of the proton are its formal effects on a neighbouring system. These can be magnified and transformed by suitable physical instruments into a symbol which can be observed by us. Quantum mechanics, however, tells us that if a proton forming part of a hydrogen atom is to interact with its environment in the way characteristic of a proton, the hydrogen atom must absorb an energetic impulse which destroys it as a bound system. Hence, in the moment in which the proton manifests its independent presence in its physical milieu, the hydrogen atom ceases to exist. The observable symbols of a hydrogen atom and of its proton-nucleus cannot be simultaneously produced. The significance attached to this is that either a hydrogen atom exists or a proton and an electron exist. What is described as a bound state of two particles does not leave the particles intrinsically unaffected by the union. It is the production of a new physical system, unique and distinct from its component parts. Its form is properly neither ele-mentary nor compound as Heisenberg has pointed out; for these terms connote a materialist or reductionist explanation which simply does not apply to the compound system. The explanation given in this paragraph of the relation of part to whole in a compound corresponds more or less to the philosophic notion of *virtual presence* as, for example used by Aquinas [2].

Energy: a "Universal Matter"?

We have briefly discussed the formal principle of a physical system: what then is its *irreducible material principle*? As energy is the only com-

---

[1] *Supra*, chap. VIII, p. 147.
[2] Cf. Aimé Forest, *La Structure métaphysique du concret selon Saint Thomas d'Aquin* (Paris: Vrin, 1956), p. 199.

mon non-vanishing factor of every physical transmutation, Heisenberg postulated that it plays the part of a "primary matter" or "universal substance". This acts like a basic field capable of being informed by any one of a series of stationary states (particle states) described by mathematical operators. This view is also put forward tentatively by Lonergan, who supports his view by pointing out that energy is a physical invariant constructed by integration but integration is a mathematical operation which tends to abolish formal structure while differentiation on the other hand complicates the formal structure [1]. For this reason, the total energy is independent of whether it is realised concretely as an atomic system or, for example, as radiation or kinetic energy of motion. The total energy is rather the limit which specifies what variety of forms is possible. In elementary particle physics, it is generally supposed that the system spends a proportion of its time in each of its possible states (or "channels") much as a canonical ensemble in thermodynamics is thought to take on every possible energy distribution. Lonergan suggests that energy may be the name given to (Aristotelian) *primary matter in the concrete*, i.e., the name for the concrete limitations of a physical system imposed by its primary matter.

While acknowledging the universal role played by energy in physical processes, we do not, for the following reasons, think that its role is analogous to that of Aristotelian and later scholastic primary matter. In the first place, energy is not the only universal determinant of physical transformations. Baryon (or atomic) number, lepton number, electric charge are also universal invariants, with this difference, however, that they may vanish for a particular system. However, there seems to be no essential difference between energy which is the invariant corresponding to Lorentz symmetry, and, say, charge, which is the invariant corresponding to a certain kind of gauge symmetry. In the second place, energy is not a simple quantity but a component of a four-vector, indicating its essential relativity to a frame of reference. The frame of reference is provided by a measuring instrument representing the physical milieu of the system in question. Energy seems rather to be a *condition of possibility* specified by the milieu and limiting what can take place in the milieu.

---

[1] B. Lonergan, *Insight* (London: 1957), pp. 443–444. The opposite view, viz., that energy is a *universal act*, is held by L. B. Guèrard des Lauriers, in "La substance sensible", *Angelicum* XXXIX (1962), pp. 40–91, 35 0–394.

The "Energy Ladder"

The operation of this condition of possibility in different milieus is illustrated well by Weisskopf's "energy ladder" [1]. The free energy capable of being exchanged between the physical system and its milieu sets limits to the character of the systems capable of existing in a stable fashion in the milieu. For example, starting at the lowest "rung" of the "energy ladder", the existence of complicated heavy molecules, like proteins and amino-acids, depends on the fact that neighbouring systems cannot exchange more than approximately 0.01 e.v. (electron volt) of energy. In this physical environment the heavy molecule reacts as a stable whole, with characteristic properties vis-à-vis the class of its interactions with its environment. Its parts are virtual, not actual, parts. The representation of it then as a structure made up of parts is from the epistemological point of view merely a symbolic representation.

If the energy capable of being exchanged between the system and its environment is increased from 0.01 e.v. to approximately 0.1 e.v., the heavy molecules become unstable and disintegrate, actualising in the process a set of simpler chemical compounds and molecules. In this state, the re-formation of a heavy molecule is not ruled out, for there is a non-zero probability of emergence of the heavy molecule out of the mixture, although there is a much larger probability of decay. As the free exchange energy is further increased even the chemical compounds break up, forming first a mixture of partly ionised atoms (at around 5 e.v.), and then a plasma of stripped nuclei (at around 10^6 e.v.) and, finally, at even higher energies, a plasma of free nucleons, electrons and other elementary particles with particle-antiparticle pair production and annihilation.

The role of energy in the "ladder" is not primarily to provide the "substance" out of which the systems in echelon are made, but rather as a condition of possibility specified by the milieu and limiting the kind of system or process permitted in this millieu.

Irreducible Matter

What then is *irreducible matter*? We arrived at the notion of "irreducible matter" by analysing the conditions of possibility of the strict object of quantum mechanics, viz., of the peculiar combination of deterministic and statistical properties which define a quantum mechanical system [2]. Irreducible matter is a constituent of physical

---

[1] Victor Weisskopf, "The Quantum Ladder", *International Science and Technology*, June, 1963, pp. 62–70.
[2] *Supra*, chap. v, pp. 109f.

reality, but no systematic effects can be attributed to it. It is the reason for the irreducibly statistical character of the observed events which represent to us the behaviour of individual systems. It is the reason for the openness of any physical form to indefinite multiplicity and the basis for the description of a physical system as a member of an equivalence class or as a virtual ensemble of systems. Beyond this, nothing more can be said. One is reminded of the famous account which Aristotle gave of *primary matter*: "*By material*", he wrote, "I mean that which is in itself not a particular thing or a quantity or anything else by which things are defined" [1]. Irreducible matter is not definable since it has no systematic consequences. But it is not nothing; its only function is to make possible the virtual ensemble which is presupposed by every quantum mechanical state functions.

Summary

This chapter treats briefly three fundamental problems which have arisen during the course of the preceding chapters. The principles for the solution of these problems are now outlined. First of all, there is the problem of the realism of scientific theories. We defend an abstractionist theory of knowledge but insist at the same time on the unity of the polymorphic cognitive activity in which we know physical reality. The structure of this activity itself reveals its realistic tendency. Secondly, we examine the kind of structure which an atomic system possesses, the relation of its parts to the whole, and the function of energy as a universal invariant. We reject the thesis that *energy* is a *universal material substance* (or *primary matter*), and propose instead that it is an ontological condition of possibility established by a milieu, which governs the kinds of systems and processes capable of taking place within the milieu.

---

[1] Met. VII (Zeta), 1029a20. Cf. also A. Mansion, *Introduction à la physique aristotélicienne* (Louvain, 1945), p. 74.

PART III

THE STRUCTURE OF PHYSICAL SCIENCE

CHAPTER TEN

LOGIC AND LANGUAGE OF SCIENCE

SECTION I: THE NATURE OF A PHYSICAL SCIENCE

The Mathematicisation of Physics

Looking back at the various problems studied in this book, one conclusion at least is evident, that the epistemological structure of modern physical science is one of extraordinary complexity. Physical science in the form with which we are familier was understandably a late arrival on the historical scene, so late in fact that the beginning of the scientific movement coincides with what historians call *modern times*.

The secret of the success of modern scientific research is the natural affinity between mathematics and natural science. The Pythagoreans are usually given the credit for this discovery, for they stumbled upon the correlation between numbers (or geometry) and certain sensible properties. They found, for example, that the notes of the scale were related to ratios of the whole numbers [1]. This was, however, no more than a minor clue to that mathematicised science which is man's most powerful tool for the transformation of the environment in which he lives. For want of a decisive and momentous insight, the physical sciences of the Greeks remained fallow for over two thousand years. Mathematical physics was delivered into man's hands, as Professor Butterfield says, not by the accumulation of new observational data but "by transpositions that were taking place inside the minds of the scientists themselves" [2].

The period of gestation for the decisive insight was the late Middle Ages. Fourteenth-century writers like Thomas Bradwardine and the Merton College group at Oxford, John Buridan and Nicholas of Oresme

---

[1] S. Sambursky, *The Physical World of the Greeks* (London: Routledge and Kegan Paul, 1956), chapter II.

[2] H. Butterfield, *The Origins of Modern Science, 1300–1800* (London): Bell, 1951), p. 1.

at Paris, Albert of Saxony and others, groped mentally for a union of mathematics and physics, which would explain *in a mathematical way* the motions of bodies. During these centuries, a new intentionality was emerging in the minds of scholars and it was one which was at variance with the established outlook of natural philosophy. For four centuries the anticipations of this new intentionality agitated the universities of Europe before it produced its first definite and unqalified success in the mechanical laws of Galileo. Western man had succeeded at last, in Butterfield's phrase, in putting on a new "thinking cap", and, in so doing, he became other than he was with consequences of breath-taking importance and originality. It was the emergence of a new power in man which, more than the religious and political differences, was to shatter the closely woven fabric of the medieval mind. What was this new "thinking cap"?

The Pythagoreans discovered that the musical qualities of sound produced by a plucked string could be mapped on to a set of whole number ratios. Since musical quality is relative to man's hearing, the whole number ratios could be referred in some obscure way to man's ability to recognise harmonies of musical sounds. It was an obscure theory for a number of reasons. First of all, it was restricted to simple arithmetical functions, for it was not clear what a complicated function of whole number ratios would sound like when converted into music – even if such a conversion were possible. Secondly, the ability to judge musical sounds differs from person to person; for it is one of those thing-to-us properties which constitute the content of an observational or descriptive concept. Modern physics does not measure observational properties but only explanatory properties, i.e., properties founded upon thing-to-thing relations. It is even doubtful whether it is meaning-ful to talk about measuring the quality of musical sounds as these are judged by the human ear. Finally, the theory was of very limited application, for it provided no set of numerical correlates for high or low frequency vibrations, which, though inaudible, are evidently of the same physical nature as the audible vibrations and differ from these only in so far as human hearing does not respond to them. It was because of all these shortcomings that Pythagorean science failed to start a scientific revolution.

The momentous insight which made modern physics possible was the discovery of a set of correlated physical properties, each founded upon a different kind of interactivity between things, which, when mapped upon the number field through suitable measuring instruments constituted a *mathematical functional*. This momentous discovery was to create a new kind of knowledge for which the centre and pole of reference was shifted out of the human observer and into things themselves, principally into macroscopic apparatus called measuring instruments which thereby became *observer-instruments*. "The Aristotelians", as Lonergan wrote, "were content to talk about the nature of light, the nature of heat, [the nature of weight, etc.... where the nature antecedently is specified by a classification based upon sensible similarity... Galileo inaugurated modern science by insisting that the nature of weight was not enough; from sensible similarity, which resides in the relation of things to our senses, one must proceed to relations that hold directly between things themselves" [1].

This procedure added three insights of incalculable importance to the Pythagorean discovery. The first was that there existed interrelated groups of physical interactions. The *second* was that the proper effects of these activities in nature, which, when "translated" by circuits, meters, etc. into observable signs, could be mapped on to a symbolic field, like the number field, through the choice of a measuring process and a measuring instrument. The *third* was that the physical interrelation could as a consequence be symbolised numerically (or at least mathematically) with the numerical (or mathematical) symbol placed in correspondence with the observable sign as numbered (or mathematically symbolised). As Professor Ladrière says of the function of mathematics: "Elle ne fournit pas seulement les procédés de raisonnement admissibles et les cadres des édifices possibles, mais elle fournit aussi les notions de base sur lesquelles ces édifices sont construits. Elle devient ainsi une sorte d'ontologie formelle générale" [2].

Conversely, the existence of a definite mathematical function between measure numbers, argued the existence of a coherent interrelated group of observable symbols and hence of physical properties symbolised.

The structure of human conceptual knowing determines that there shall be two types of physical theories: *deterministic theories* and *statistical theories*. It was the discovery of the quantum theory which brought the realisation that the two kinds of theories might be combined in one formalism.

For the Pythagoreans, the mathematicised musical quality was an observational property, a property-for-us. A physical property in

---

[1] B. Lonergan, *Insight* (London, 1957), p. 38.
[2] Jean Ladrière, "La philosophie des mathématiques", *Rev. Phil. Louv.*, LVII (1959), p. 617.

modern science, however, is *defined* within the systematic totality of correlated physical properties with which and in relation to which it is defined. This is its *explanatory definition*. Each property has in addition an *operational description*, which describes how an appropriate experimental measuring process might be performed, and *observable criteria*, which manifest its presence in the real world, and also provide the (usually numerical) symbol – e.g., a pointer reading – through which it is included in a mathematical theory. It should be noted that only the *explanatory definition* defines *in the strict sense* what the property is: the *operational description* and the *observable criteria* are extrinsic to the property defined. *Observable criteria* merely constitute part of the symbol though which the property manifests its presence in the real world.

Since the scientist's presence in the world is through his body which is a thing in the world, he may sometimes obtain direct intuitive experience through his sensibility of some types of physical properties; as, for example, of light, force, etc. Such intuitive experience can found an observational concept of the property based upon the typical effect of the property on human sensibility or on the typical use it might have for man. This cannot, however, be identified with either the explanatory definition or the operational description or the observable criteria of the physical property. The explanatory definition and the operational description are clearly different from this new concept. The observable criteria, moreover, are also different from it, since they describe one of the *symbols of the property in nature*, produced in an instrument and not directly in human sensibility.

Space and Time

The above-mentioned distinction applies to the difference between the physical concept of space and time – in so far as these are explanatory concepts – and the concepts of space and time based upon the structure of human perception and activity in the World-for-man. The first attempt to define explanatorily the structure of space and time was made by Einstein when he proposed the special and general theory of relativity. Up to that time, space and time were conceived to be absolute pre-conditions of physical events and processes. Space was the container of simultaneous events; time ordered sequences of eveants in an orderly way; but neither space nor time was founded upon an interaction between the events themselves. Absolute Space and Absolute Time were thought to belong to the objective and irreducible elements in any explanation, and probably would have remained this way but for the crisis in physics arising from the non-invariance of Maxwell's electromagnetic equations under the Galilean transformation group which defined the properties of Absolute Space and Absolute Time. Under the influence of Mach, Einstein was led to question the givenness and irreducibility of physical space and time and eventually to analyse the space-time structure presupposed by the scientific method.

Such an attempt, we believe, was bound to be made and was even demanded by the logical structure of the scientific method. The physicist's view of explanation is to construct a World-for-things, viewing reality, as it were, from the point of perspective of an instrumental observer which becomes the centre of its own space and time. Since an instrument is not endowed with an imagination and a memory to situate all things simultaneously and ideally with respect to one another, its "experience" of its physical ambience must be based upon the ways it can actually receive influences from other things and influence other things in turn.

Early in this century it was discovered that the fastest and most universal means of transmitting such influences was, in fact – at least on the macroscopic scale – the electro-magentic or photon field. Einstein proposed in the special theory of relativity to identify distance with distance-as-measured-by-light-pulses, and time intervals with time intervals-as-measured-by-light-pulses. Since the photon exchange between object and instrument takes a finite interval of time to pass between them, Einstein concluded that the distance between the two things must be related to the time taken by a photon to pass from one to the other. Let *concrete physical space* be defined as space-for-a-particular-observer-instrument, and *concrete time* as time-for-a-particular-observer-instrument; these are the ordered manifold of distance and time intervals as measured by this observer-instrument. Any macroscopic thing in nature, however, can serve as an observer-instrument and so become the centre of perspective of the World-for-things. We are led to ask then, how the particular concrete space and time of one observer-instrument is related to the concrete space and time of another observer-instrument. Making the simplest assumption possible, Einstein found that the two spaces and times were related by a coordinate transformation belonging to the Poincaré (inhomogeneous Lorentz) group. In the later general theory of relativity, more complicated transformation groups were considered, but in all forms of the theory of relativity, the basic measure of distance is reduced to a time-like measurement on a standard clock [1]. The basic structure of space and time in expressed by the conservation of a scalar invariant (ds^2) under the continuous transformation group.

The Primacy of the Instrument

The new kind of mathematicised physics was not simply a rival to person-centered knowledge; for the person-centered world of observation is a condition for the existence of this knowledge. But beside the World-for-us, a new aspect of our World was discovered which was thing-centered; that is, centered on a part of nature itself. A measuring instrument in the new outlook played the part of an "observer-instrument" which "felt" and "observed" reality and "spoke" of its "experiences" to the scientist through the "language" of observable physical symbols; for the new science consciously took the point of view of an instrument immersed in nature. Colours, sounds, etc., which constituted the World-for-us, took on a new symbolic character and became a "language" which "spoke" of the physical structure and interactions behind them. The scientist translated these into mathematical symbols, in which form they entered a mathematical theory which, as an intelligible whole, gave meaning to its terms.

How does an instrument – as a substitute observer immersed in nature itself – "speak" of its "experiences"? The measured property produces a macroscopic effect in the instrument; as, for example, a pointer reading on a scale, a "click" of a counter, or a track in a bubble chamber. This macroscopic effect is a material sign. A sign has a double reality: its *material reality* as a pointer, sound or bubble track, and an *intentional reality* proper to it as a sign, viz., as indicating something beyond its material reality; as, for example, a magnetic field intensity (the pointer), a charged particle (the "click"), or an elementary particle like the Omega-minus (the bubble track). Intentional reality is the mode of being of a sign as such. The act which confers intentional reality on a material sign, moreover, is not formally in the instrument, which is unconscious and devoid of the power of uttering significant signs, but formally in the mind of the scientist. The intentional reality of sign is the neomatic correlate to an act of inquiring intelligence which is not content with what it sees, but looks for its explanation.

Instrumental data is more than a sign, it is a *symbol* of a physical

[1] Cf., J. L. Synge, *Relativity: The General Theory* (Amsterdam: 1960), chap. III.

property; for it *stands for* the property, as words in a language stand for the things they signify. Words in a human language, however, are conventional symbols; observable symbols in physics, such as the ones we have been considering, are *natural symbols*, since in a well-designed measuring process, they are uniquely determined by the interaction with the object. The "language" appropriate to an instrument when it "speaks" is a *"physicalistic language"*, in so far as it "translates" the hidden state of the object into a uniquely-determined sensible sign [1].

The scientist, observing this sign, translates it in turn into a linguistic statement; as, for example, "This is the signature of an Omega-minus particle". This latter translation is not, however, a physicalistic one, for two reasons: 1) it describes more than the mere material reality of the data, i.e., it is *not* a mere *object language expression*, and 2) the data itself does not determine a unique linguistic statement. The statement "This is the signature of an Omega-minus particle" refers to a material object, viz., the signature, but only as a symbol of something which is not given as a material object, viz., the Omega-minus particle [2]. Moreover, the instrumental data does not determine *of itself* a unique linguistic statement; for it responds to the type of question formulated by the scientist. Of itself, the instrument is "dumb"; it waits to be questioned by the scientist, and the form of the question structures its response. For example, the data may evoke a mere description of its material reality (a bubble chamber track), or an explanation of its intentional reality (a signature of an Omega-minus particle), or an assertion or denial of a hypothesis (the Eightfold Way). The instrument then responds to the noetic intention of the scientist; it does not create it. It "speaks" only if "questioned"; and the structure of its response mirrors the structure of the "question asked" of it.

Many physicists, for want of a better theory of knowledge, adopt a form of psycho-physical parallelism which entails a unique physicalistic translation of physical events into linguistic statements [3]. It is clear from what has just been said that this is not a correct account of scientific knowledge or language.

---

[1] Cf. K. Popper, *Conjectures and Refutations* (London: Routledge and Kegan Paul, 1963), pp. 296–297 for a discussion of the language of an instrument.

[2] The existence of the Omega-minus particle (mass, 1678; isotopic spin, 3/2; parity, plus) was predicted by a scheme of symmetry known as the "Eightfold Way". The prediction was made by Gell-Mann, Y Ne'eman, Salam and Ward. The discovery of the particle was announced by R. P. Schutt and his team at Brookhaven Laboratory in *Phys. Rev. Letters*, Feb. 24, XII (1964), 204–206.

[3] For example, N. Bohr, J. von Neumann, E. Wigner, S. Watanabe and others. Cf., N. Bohr, *Atomic Theory and the Description of Nature* (Cambridge: 1961), pp. 24, 115–119.

SECTION II: THE LANGUAGE OF PHYSICS

Two Languages

The distinction and interrelation between observation and explanation in physics can also be explained from the point of view of language. A language is composed of a vocabulary, syntactic rules governing the way words are connected into phrases and sentences, and a dictionary of correct usage governing the application of linguistic expressions (words, phrases, sentences, etc.) to their referents.

A language originates in a noetic viewpoint and is the instrumental expression of this viewpoint. The World described by a language is the neomatic response to the originating noetic orientation. Now the noetic orientation of a physicist is twofold: 1) he works with, describes and observes pieces of apparatus and their behaviour, in so far as these are parts of a *World-for-him*, and 2) he expresses what happens in nature from the perspective of an instrument, immersed in nature; the World to which he orients himself is one structured about things; it is a World-for-things [1]. Corresponding to this twofold noetic orientation of the physicist one expects to find, and one does in fact find, two languages: an *observation language* to express operational and observational concepts, and an *explanatory language* to express explanatory concepts.

It would seem to be at first sight plausible that the distinction should be caused by the existence of two kinds of referents for physical statements, viz., observable facts in their material reality and theoretical constructs (like electrons and Omega-minus particles) to explain these facts. One may be led uncritically to assume that the observable symbols are to be described by an observation language, while the theoretical constructs are to be described by a theoretical language. This indeed is commonly held by philosophers, as, e.g., by Wilgred Sellars, Reichenbach, Carnap and others. We do not think it correct for the following reasons:

1) Even theoretical constructs, like electrons, are observable although only indirectly and by interpretation. This was implied in the content of Heisenberg's original insight that only *observables* should enter into the structure of physics. Observation language is not

---

[1] Or more correctly a *World-of-things-to-things-for-him*, as we pointed out in note 1, p. 59.

restricted, therefore, to the material sensible sign, but correct observation statements can be formulated even about theoretical entities.
When a physicist observes, for example, a track in a bubble chamber,
he does not merely study material marks, but he observes them as the
signature of some particle, and his noetic intention is *through the
observable signature to the particle*. Such noetic activity results in
making particles and other theoretical constructs a part of the World-
for-us; they take on the character of being given in perception –
although of course not "given primordially in perception" [1] – but none
the less rationally given by interpretation.

2) Moreover, the physical interaction between bodies given directly
in perception can also be explained theoretically. One thinks of
Eddington's two tables: one, the solidly perceived table; the other,
a chaos of vibrating infinitesimal particles and constituted mostly
of emptiness [2]. Precise analysis shows that no physical property or
thing, in so far as they are a part of an explanatory physical context,
is *per se* representable in sensibility. It is illegitimate to try to visualise
the table *as explained*, for visualisation belongs to description and not
to explanation. Whatever is visualised is a property-for-us; explanatory
properties are not properties-for-us, but properties-for-things [3]. Hence,
while the table has two sets of predicates each of which is correct,
notice must be taken of the fact that they belong to different languages.
It can be misleading to translate explanatory predicates into such
typical terms as "chaos" and "emptiness". In our view both the
accounts given above are correct; both tables are real, and they have
one identical referent.

The difference between *observation language* and *explanatory language*,
then, is not that they deal with different sets of referents, but that
they consider the same set within different contexts. One considers
them within the context of a World-for-us, while the other considers
them within the context of a World-for-things. For this reason we
prefer the pair of terms "observation language" and "explanatory
language", for they do not suggest contrast and opposition to the
same extent as the more usual alternative pair, viz., "observation
language" and "theoretical language".

It may be objected that theoretical entities like elementary particles,
etc., are ontologically on a different footing from objects like those

---

[1] Edmund Husserl, *Ideas* (London: Allen and Unwin, 1931), p. 52.
[2] Sir Arthur Eddington, *The Nature of the Physical World* (Camb. Univ. Press, 1928), p. XIV.
[3] *Supra*, pp. 59–61.

given directly in perception, and that this distinction should be recognised linguistically by having one language for observed bodies and another for theoretical constructs like elementary particles. This apparently is the opinion of W. Sellars, Carnap and many others. We answer that we too recognise that there is a difference in the ontological status of the two classes of objects, but in our view this difference does not constitute the real differences between the two languages. A language expresses a systematic whole, that is, a totality of referents related to one another in a particular way. "Observation language" and "explanatory language" represent, as we have said, different systematic totalities; but the classes of object to which they refer are both *real*. Their different ontological status results not from the supposition that one set is real while the other set is ideal (or purely mental), but from the fact that different kinds of criteria are used according to which their reality is known to us. In the case of bodies given in perception, it is the coherence of what is given with the rest of experience (not, of course, merely as a given coherence – for the dream-world too has its coherence – but as one whose coherence is critically and reasonably accepted). The criterion of a theoretical construct like an elementary particle, on the other hand, is more complex and involves; 1) the ability to make virtually unconditioned judgements about the truth of a physical theory, and 2) the establishment of a connection between certain observable criteria and the reality of the physical entities which constitute the physical explanation. The same essential epistemological problem arises for all physical theories, whether one discusses the reality of mass, force and gravitation or the reality of mesons, neutrinos and Omega-particles. The only difference between the two sets of cases is that it is more difficult to satisfy the strategic criteria in the second set than in the first set.

Others, as we have said, have different views. We cite Wilfred Sellars as an example [1]. He holds that the correspondence rules which form the "bridge" between the observation language and what he calls the theoretical language "appear in the material mode as statements to the effect that objects of the observational framework *do not really exist – there really are no such things*". Such a viec is wonsistent with the epistemological position that reality is constituted, or at least manifested, by the relation of exteriority between a subject and a fully constituted phenomenal object. We are opposed to this view. For us, the criterion

---

[1] Wilfred Sellars, "The Language of Theories" in *Current Issues in the Philosophy of Science*, ed. by G. Feigl and G. Maxwell (New York: Holt, Rinehart and Winston, 1961), p. 76.

of a real thing is the *rationality* of the unconditioned affirmation of an object presented in sensation, whether directly or under its observable symbol, and understood whether in relation to ourselves (descriptively) or in relation to other things (explanatorily). This implies a meaning of the term "reality" different from that of Wilfred Sellars. It also implies a different criterion for the discernment of what is real.

Summary

This chapter puts into systematic form some of the clues to the nature of a physical theory, which have arisen during the course of the previous chapters. First of all, we treat of the two parts of a physical science: the formal mathematical theory whose function is to describe a World-for-things, and the experimental (operational and observational) part which makes this World-for-things, also a World-for-us. Secondly, we discuss the space and time of physics, distinguishing it from the and time of perception. Thirdly, we describe the key concept of an observable symbol. Finally, we give an account of the two languages used by a physicist: the explanatory language and the observation language.

APPENDIX

LAW OF SUPERPOSITION OF WAVE FUNCTIONS

It was found experimentally that while the individual impact of, say an elementary particle on a screen is granular and discrete like the impact of a particle, still the manner in which it interacts with an apparatus or even with itself (e.g., in a beam of very low intensity) can only be described on the basis of a wave-like law like that of the wave theory of light. The characteristic property of wave motion in a medium is that, if different wave motions are superimposed, their amplitudes add or cancel according as their phases are equal or opposite. This wave-like law of superposition gives rise to the characteristic wave-like properties of interference fringes, diffraction patterns, etc.[1]. The evidence for the dual wave and particle nature of all matter and even of light has been refined and re-inforced by experiments like those of Janossy on small dust particles and on light beams of very low intensity [2]. Using a light beam of very low intensity, he found that single photons were capable of interfering with themselves in a two-slit experiment. By using very small dust particles which behaved like classical particles in the same experiment, he was able to rule out alternate explanations of the interference postulated by the wave-particle duality of the quantum theory.

These results, as well as the great success which the quantum theory has enjoyed, provide very persuasive evidence that the *law of superposition* of wave functions (or physical states) is basically correct. However, when combined with the usual statistical interpretation of the wave function, the axiom leads to the strange and paradoxical results associated with the "reduction of the wave packet", which we

[1] The original experimental evidence for the dual wave and particle nature of all matter and also of light is described in Heisenberg's *Physical Principles etc.*, chap. I, or in any text-book of physics.

[2] L. Janossy, "The physical Aspects of the Wave-Particle Problem", *Acta Physica Hungarica*, I (1952), pp. 423–467; IV (1955); *Nuovo Cimento*, VI (1957); *Hungar. Acad. of Sci.*, 1957. An account of these experiments is given by F. Bopp in *Werner Heisenberg und die Physik unserer Zeit*, ed. F. Bopp, pp. 145–147.

outlined in chapter V. So paradoxical do the results seem to some physicists that they would be willing to suppress this axiom entirely, or change it substantially, if this could be done without sacrificing the explanatory and predictive value of the quantum theory in its present form. Wigner has suggested the introduction of non-linear equations; Janossy has experimented with a damping factor to ensure that after a sufficient lapse of time the interference of superposed states is suppressed.

According to the "orthodox" interpretation of the quantum theory, the act of observation has the effect of immediately suppressing the interference of the component waves in the wave function by actu-alising one component and suppressing all the others. This actualisation depends on the fact that the observer is a conscious subject. If he were not, but merely a piece of unconscious apparatus, no reduction of the wave packet would take place and the interference of the superposed component waves would continue with effects different from what they would have been if the reduction had taken place. To illustrate the difference analytically between a *pure case* (characterised by the interference of the component waves) and a *mixture* (in which the component waves do not interfere), we consider the following example.

Let a physical system be capable of existing in only two states S_1 and S_2 (say, the two orientations of spin in the direction of the z-axis). Let it be prepared in such a way that its wave function S is the following superposition of the two states:

$$S = aS_1 + bS_2$$

where

$$|a|^2 + |b|^2 = 1$$

Case I: So long as the system is *not observed*, it will have a *pure case* statistical matrix [1].

$$U = P_S = \begin{vmatrix} |a|^2 & ab^* \\ a^*b & |b|^2 \end{vmatrix} \tag{I}$$

Case II: If the system is *observed*, then it is reduced to a *mixture* of the states S_1 and S_2; S_1 occuring with a probability $|a|^2$ and S_2 with a probability $|b|^2$. Such a mixture is represented by the in-homogeneous statistical matrix.

$$V = |a|^2 P_{S1} + |b|^2 P_{S2} = \begin{vmatrix} |a|^2 & 0 \\ 0 & |b|^2 \end{vmatrix} \tag{II}$$

[1] Cf. L. D. Landau and E. M. Lifschitz, *Quantum Mechanics: Non-relativistic Theory* (London: Pergamon Press, 1958), pp. 35–38; J. von Neumann, *Mathematical Foundations etc.*, pp. 328–329.

Consider now a physical quantity represented by the operator Q which does not commute with the z-direction of spin (e.g., the x-direction of spin). Let the eigen value $+1$ be associated with the eigen vector $\frac{1}{\sqrt{2}}(S_1 + S_2)$, and let the eigen value -1 be associated with the eigen vector $\frac{1}{\sqrt{2}}(S_1 - S_2)$. Then,

$$Q = \begin{vmatrix} 0 & 1 \\ 1 & 0 \end{vmatrix}$$

The expectation value of Q in Case I is [1],

$$\text{Tr}(UQ) = \text{Tr}(P_SQ) = a^*b + ab^*$$

The expectation value of Q in Case II is,

$$\text{Tr}(VQ) = \text{Tr}(|a|^2 P_{S1}Q + |b|^2 P_{S2}Q) = 0$$

The difference in the two cases is due entirely to the fact that in Case I, the superposed eigen states S_1 and S_2 interfere, while in Case II, the interference between S_1 and S_2 has been suppressed.

Entropy and Information

The difference between a pure state and a mixture is also revealed when they are submitted to an analysis according to the principles of *information or cybernetic theory* [2]. The *information* present in a given physical situation is measured by the entropy function [3]

$$H = -\sum_i p_i \log_2 p_i$$

where p_i is the probability that a certain observable signal (represented say, by the value z_i of a meter-indicator) be received and the base of the logarithm is 2. *Information* is used here in the technical sense of communications theory and refers not to what is consciously adverted to in the physical situation but to what could be communicated by this physical situation, that is, its potentiality as a communications symbol. The application of the formula H to the simple case considered above throws an interesting light on the mutual relationship between

[1] Landau and Lifschitz, *ibid.*, Von Neumann, *loc. cit.*, p. 316.
[2] Cf., C. Shannon and W. Weaver, *The Mathematical Theory of Communications* (Urbana: University of Illinois Press, 1963); L. Brillouin, *La science et la théorie de l'information* (Paris: Masson, 1959).
[3] Also, and probably more fittingly, called *negentropy* by, e.g., Brillouin.

a pure state and a mixture and one which confirms the epistemological analysis made in the text.

Consider a simple system represented by the (time independent) pure state vector $S = aS_1 + bS_2$ (where neither a nor b is zero). The orthogonal base of this representation can be changed to one in which S is one of the base vectors, and in which the other base vector is represented by $S^* = -bS_1 + aS_2$. If now apparatus is employed which is so designed as to distinguish between S and S^*, the entropy of the physical situation constituted by the object *plus* this physical milieu is o; since the probability of S is 1 and the probability of S^* is o. The information then contained in this situation is o. Note that the complete physical situation is one composed of the object and an experimental context whose nature and existence is due to the free choice and initiative of the scientist himself.

On the other hand, if a different measuring apparatus is chosen whose function is to discriminate between the states S_1 and S_2, then the pure state formulation is to be replaced, as we have explained, by a mixture of the states S_1 and S_2, where S_1 and S_2 have respectively the statistical weights $|a|^2$ and $|b|^2$. The entropy of the new situation (i.e., of the object plus the new apparatus) is

$$H = -\,|a|^2 \log |a|^2 - |b|^2 \log |b|^2 > 0$$

The transformation from a pure state to a mixture involves then an increase in entropy from o to some positive value. The maximum value of the entropy change (or the maximum increase in information) is evidently one unit (one bit), and this is obtained when $|a|^2 = |b|^2 = \frac{1}{2}$.

This simple example illustrates two very important aspects of the measuring process: (i) the increase in entropy associated with the "reduction of the wave packet" and attributed theoretically to the suppression of correlations between the component states S_1 and S_2, and (ii) the fact that the difference between the two cases is due to the different experimental contexts in which the object makes its appearance. The latter depends on a free *choice* on the part of the scientist which is to be followed presumably by his activity in setting up the appropriate apparatus. The formulae, as we have shown, refer to the *total physical situation* in which the object is placed and not merely to the object taken in some absolute, real or abstract sense. The range of response of the apparatus plays the part of a *signal channel* which is modulated by the physical interaction between the object and the chosen apparatus. The *signal* itself is what we called the *observable symbol.* The entropy then in each case, which measures the information content of the measuring process, is the signal entropy, and refers to a holistic physical situation compounded of the physical object and one of a variety of physical situations subject to the experimenter's choice. The "reduction of the wave packet" then is nothing more than the expression of the scientist's choice of a measuring process which is different from the means used to prepare the pure state.

GLOSSARY
OF PHILOSOPHICAL AND SCIENTIFIC TERMS

PART I: PHILOSOPHICAL TERMS [1]

Abstraction: the activity of achieving an insight into empirical data and of defining the insight in a concept. See *concept*.

Affirmation: the act of assertion. It corresponds to the 'is' in the proposition "This is so". The assertion may be *absolutely unconditioned*, i.e., if no conditions are attached (guaranteed, for example, by the principle of contradiction), or *virtually unconditioned*, i.e., if subject to conditions which are, however, in fact fulfilled. The fulfilment of these conditions is the epistemological ground for the rationality of the affirmation. The fulfilled conditions are called the *evidence* for the affirmation. See *probability (evidential), formal objectivity*.

Being: the most basic transcendental ontological perfection; it is expressed by the strong value of the verb 'to be'. Epistemologically, it is the ultimate horizon intended by every complete act of human knowing. Being, however, is constituted by the act of knowing but the act of knowing adds to being the relation of *truth*. See *judgement, formal objectivity, affirmation, truth, idealism*.

Body: A thing which is directly perceptible and whose relation to a subject is one of exteriority. In the strict sense, a body is a thing related to empirical experience: in the broad sense, a body also includes the limiting conceptual models of classical particle and classical field. See *thing, empirical objectivity*.

---

[1] The definitions which follow indicate the author's use of the terms and are intended to be a short guide to the epistemological and ontological position which the author is assuming. The basic position adopted by the author corresponds to a large extent with that of Bernard J. Lonergan's *Insight* from which some of the terminology has been taken. The author has also used A. Lalande's *Vocabulaire technique et critique de la philosophie* (P.U.F., 9th ed. 1962) in compiling this glossary.

Causal or deterministic theory: in the primary sense, it is any theory which enables one to predict a definite spatio-temporal happening (usually the observed value of a variable) when the initial conditions required by the theory are fully known at some prior epoch. In a secondary sense, it is any theory which allows the perdiction either of a spatio-temporal event or of the form of a state-function when the initial conditions required by the theory are known at a prior epoch.

Causality (Kantian category): the necessary and universal association of an antecedent phenomenon A (cause) and a subsequent phenomenon B (effect) schematised by the regularity of their association in intuition.

Cause (ontological): a being or a principle of being which (by its causality) produces or contributes to the production of a being (the effect). This is the traditional philosophical usage and is to be distinguished carefully from the sense of *cause* used in modern scientific writings and which is the same as that used in the text of this work (see *scientific cause* below). Causes are either *extrinsic* to the effect as, e.g., the efficient, exemplary and final causes, or *intrinsic* to the effect as, e.g., the material and formal causes. An *efficient cause* is the proper cause of the *existence* of the effect, i.e. it answers the question: What produced this effect? The *final cause* is the proper cause of the *activity* of the efficient cause and answers the question: Why was this produced? The *material cause* is that *out of which* the effect is produced and answers the question: What is the effect made of? The *formal cause* is the *pattern* or *intrinsic relationship of parts* within the effect and answers the question: What kind of effect has been produced? The *exemplary cause* is the *model* (mental or material) which an intelligent agent has in mind when he acts.

Cause (scientific): a restricted application of the notion of *formal cause* (see above) to regular temporal antecedent-subsequent pairs of events. The antecedent event is the *cause* relative to the subsequent event which is called the *effect*. An event is any precise spatio-temporal happening. Unless otherwise implied, this is the sense generally used by the author in the text.

Classical physical system: one which is governed by causal or deterministic laws in the primary sense. See *causal theory*.

Concept or idea: a Universal, i.e., the content of an intellectual act of defining the content of an act of insight (or understanding) into empirical data; the reflection which follows the insight exhibits the definition as universal, that is, as not restricted to these particular data.

Criterion of truth: the epistemological conditions to be satisfied in order that a proposition can be rationally affirmed as virtually or absolutely unconditioned. See *affirmation, truth, epistemology*.

Critical philosophy: the philosophy of Immanuel Kant (1724–1804).

Definition: the content of the concept which answers the question: "What kind of thing is this?" See *concept, implicit definition*.

Description: an account of how something appears to the senses or of the uses it can be put to or of the characteristic sensible signs by which it can be recognized.

Empiricism: an epistemological doctrine (opposed to *rationalism*) which denies the existence (or at least the validity) of *a priori* synthetic principles of knowledge different from what is impressed in immediate sense experience or from generalizations based on this. For empiricism, direct sense experience gives both the meaning and the criterion of reality judgements. See *rationalism*.

Epistemology: the critical study of the logical and psychological structure of human knowing activities with a view to discerning (i) their internal structure, (ii) the functions performed by the different parts of the act of knowing in the specification of the total meaningful content, (iii) the reliability of various kinds of knowing activities, and (iv) criteria for the valid assertion of truth.

Essentialism: a form of rationalism. See *rationalism*.

Experience: sense experience as, for example, impressions on the external senses, or sense images or representations in the imagination; it is that part of consciousness which represents its object in space and time i.e., here and now. See empirical objectivity.

Explanatory concept: a definition based upon thing-to-thing relations. It is usually associated with implicit definition. See *concept, definition implicit definition*.

Idealism: the epistemological doctrine (opposed to realism) which tends to assert that *being* means *being thought* or *being the object of conscious awareness* and so to deny the existence of anything which is not the object of conscious awareness or not subject to the strict exigencies of consciousness. See *realism*.

Idea: see *concept*.

Implicit definition: the definition of one element of a complex concept (usually a closed set of mutually defined thing-to-thing relations as e.g., in a mathematical theory) by reference to the total concept. See *concept, definition*.

Instrumentalism: an epistemological doctrine combining agnosticism about the realistic value of (scientific) concepts with the view that their value is purely practical and utilitarian. See *positivism, empiricism*.

Intelligible object: same as concept. See *concept*.

Intentionality-structure of an act of (scientific) knowing: the orientation of a human knowing (neotic) subject towards a horizon of knowledge constituted by a certain ordered context of objects usually given or to be given in experience (neomata). It is the logical structure of a question and represents a reality-outline to be filled by answers to be obtained usually through empirical investigation. See *objectivity, reality, World*.

Hylomorphism: the (Aristotelian) ontological doctrine that every material substance is composed of two distinct but inseparable ontological principles, primary matter and substantial form. See *primary matter, substantial form*.

Judgement: the complete act of knowing, i.e., the assertion of a meaning which itself is polymorphic, that is, made up of conceptual and experiential elements.

Meaning: the content of what is asserted by a declarative proposition.

Mechanism: the ontological doctrine that all material beings are completely reducible to atomic elements in motion or joined together in characteristic spatial configurations.

Noumenon: or thing-in-itself: a being, viz., some thing or principle whose existence does not depend on its being an object of human conscious awareness.

Objective: possessing some form of objectivity. See *Objectivity* below.

Objectivity: the property of being an object of an act of human conscious awareness.

Objectivity, empirical: the kind of objectivity based upon the opposition of exteriority between a knowing subject and an object given in perception (empirical object). If precision is made from the act of affirmation, we have a *phenomenal object* (or *phenomenon*); if the act of affirmation is included, we have a *bodily object* (or *body*). See *body, thing, phenomenon*.

Objectivity, formal: the property of being the object of a complete act of knowing, i.e., of being a virtually or absolutely unconditioned object of knowledge. This is the *object in the strict or formal sense.* Its intention is to express *what is,* i.e. what belongs to *being,* (the *noumenon* or *thing-in-itself*).

Objectivity, public: the property of being an object of knowledge for a certain community; hence, of being a possible topic for communication between members of the community. There are two kinds of public objectivity: (i) the public objectivity of a conceptual definition and (ii) the public objectivity of a reality in the community's common World. See *reality, World, definition, concept.*

Observable symbol: an event occurring within the measuring process which (i) manifests the reality of a thing or of a property of a thing, and (ii) which can be calibrated and so used within a mathematical theory for the purposes of implicit definition, deduction and prediction.

Observational concept: a description of some thing (or of some property of a thing) or of some characteristic observable symbols of the thing (or of its property). See *observable symbol.*

Ontology: the philosophical science which deals with beings under the transcendental aspects of being, existence, oneness, truth, etc.

Operational concept: the prescription for the type of actions to be performed (for example, in the measuring process) in order to actualize or make manifest the term or relation under consideration. The manifestation of the term or relation takes place in the measuring process under some recognizable observable symbol, as, for example, a meter reading. See *observable symbol.*

Operationalism: a form of positivism (or instrumentalism) proposed by P. W. Bridgman which holds that a physical variable represents nothing more than the experimental procedures used to measure it.

Parallelism, psycho-physical: the theory that between physical reality and the mental awareness of it there exists the kind of relation (or parallelism) which exists between a text and a translation or coding of the same text.

Phenomenon: experience subsumed under some intellectual category or conceptual unification, prescinding however from the affirmation of being. See *affirmation, experience, concept, formal objectivity.*

Positivism: the epistemological doctrine professing agnosticism about the realistic value of (scientific) concepts.

Primary Matter (Aristotelian): the universal material cause in nature, i.e., the intrinsic principle of a material being to which no formal (i.e. intelligible or systematic) effects can be attributed. See *cause (ontological)*, *substantial form*.

Probability (mathematical) of an event: the ideal frequency of occurrence of this type of event within any large sample of similar but independent situations.

Probability (evidential) of an assertion: the degree to which the evidence in question supports the particular assertion, that is, brings it close to the status of a virtually unconditioned assertion. Other names for this kind of probability are *assertability*, *credibility*, *reasonableness*. See *affirmation*.

Property-for-things: a property whose definition connotes a complex of relations centred on a thing or instrument.

Property-for-us: a property whose definition connotes a complex of relations centred on the subject.

Rationalism: epistemological doctrine (opposed to *empiricism*) which asserts that the only source of true knowledge is the set of evident, incontrovertible, universal and necessary *a priori* principles of the understanding; according to rationalism, sense impressions afford merely a confused picture of reality or serve merely as a criterion or occasion of recognizing truth which is found therefore only in purely intelligible objects. See *empiricism*.

Realism: the epistemological doctrine (opposed to idealism) which affirms the capacity of the human knowing activity to represent to itself truly independently of human conscious awareness of it as an object of thought. See *idealism*, *formal objectivity*, *noumenon*.

Reality: whatever is asserted as belonging to the subject's World. See *World*.

Reality (Kantian category): a pure concept of the understanding schematized by a filling of the empty form of intuition, viz., of time.

Subjective: belonging to or deriving from a conscious subject, or lacking some specific kind of objectivity. See *objectivity*.

Subjectivity: the character of being subjective. See *subjective*.

Substance (Kantian category): a pure concept of the understanding schematized by permanence of reality in time.

Substance (ontological): a kind of being which exists of itself and is the subject of attributes (or accidents).

Substantial form: the intelligible unifying (or formal) ontological principle in a material substance, correlative to primary matter. See *primary matter*.

Thing: a unity, identity, whole and stable subject of attributes, whether these be directly perceptible (as for a *body*) or only indirectly perceptible through the interpretation of observable symbols. See *body, empirical objectivity, formal objectivity, observable symbol.*

Transcendental deduction: the search for the *a priori* (subjective) conditions of possibility of experience and the philosophical method characteristic of critical philosophy. See *critical philosophy.*

Truth (logical): the relation of conformity between the strict object of knowledge (possessed of formal objectivity) and the being or principle of being represented by this object.

Truth (ontological): the relation of conformity between a being and its definition as formulated by the mind.

World: the horizon of all actual or possible objects (in the strict or formal sense) of human empirical investigation. See *reality, formal objectivity.*

World-for-things (or World-of-things-to-things-for-us): the horizon of reality appropriate to scientific explanations.

World-for-us: the horizon of everyday reality.

PART 2: SCIENTIFIC TERMS

Complementarity: the theory, due to Bohr, that a microscopic system has a particle aspect and a wave aspect both of which, while mutually incompatible, are equally fundamental. See the text for a full discussion.

Completeness Principle: the principle which states that the physical state of a system is completely described by any *complete set of commuting observables*, i.e., by any set comprising one from every pair of conjugate canonical observables. See *observable, conjugate variables.*

Configuration space (for an n-particle system): an abstract Euclidean space of 3n dimensions.

Conjugate variables (or observables): a pair of variables (or observables) represented by non-commuting operators.

Coordinate space: 3-dimensional space in which experimental observations take place.

Correspondence Principle: the (mainly regulative) principle requiring that the results of quantum physics pass into those of classical physics in marginal cases of large quantum numbers and massive systems. See the discussion in the text.

Correspondence, rules of (or rules of interpretation): the prescription for interpreting the symbols of a mathematico-physical theory in operational or observational terms.

Eigen function (of an operator): a function which is mapped upon itself (except for multiplication by a constant called the *eigen value*) by the operator in question. The eigen functions of an operator represent the observable physical states of a system; the eigen value corresponding to a particular eigen function is the value which a measurement performed on the system in the given eigen state would yield.

Eigen state of an observable: a physical state represented by an eigen function of the corresponding operator. See *observable*.

Eigen value (of an operator): see *eigen function*.

Expectation value (of a variable): the theoretical average value (of a variable) when a large number of measurements are made on exactly similar systems.

Indeterminacy Relations (or Uncertainty Principle of Heisenberg): the theorem that the product of the standard deviations of a pair of canonically conjugate variables, as, e.g., momentum and position, is never less than h (Planck's constant). See *standard deviation*, *conjugate variables*.

Mixture: the state of a (generally virtual) ensemble of physical systems in different states and representable accordingly by a density matrix (an array of probabilities enabling the distribution of systems in different states to be calculated).

Observable: any measurable physical quantity: represented in the quantum theory by a hypermaximal Hermitian linear operator (i.e., one having a soluble eigen value equation with real eigen values). See *eigen value, operator*.

Operator: a linear operator in the mathematical theory of abstract Hilbert spaces; every physical observable is represented by a Hermitian operator and every physical state is represented by a ray (wave function) in this theory. See *observable, wave function*.

Probability wave: see *wave packet*.

Projection postulate: the postulate relating to the theory of measurement that the immediate effect of the measuring process is to produce one of the eigen states of the measured observable.

Psi-function: see *wave function*.

Pure case (or pure state): the state of a single physical system representable by a wave function.

Reduction of the wave packet: the 'contraction' of a superposition state to one of the component eigen states resulting from the act of observation which completes the measuring process. See text for a full discussion. See also *superposition state, eigen state.*

Schrödinger's equation: the differential equation which describes the development in time of a physical system when its initial state is given.

Standard deviation (of a set of values x_i, $i = 1, \ldots, N$): if $\bar{x}$ is the average of the set x_i, then the standard deviation (s) is defined as

$$s = \sum_{i=1}^{N} \sqrt{\frac{(x_i - \bar{x})^2}{N}}$$

State function: see *wave function.*

Superposition state: the state of a single physical system which is represented by a linear function of several wave functions usually of simultaneous eigen functions of a complete set of observables. See *eigen function, completeness.*

Virtual ensemble: one system considered as a random sample of one from a set of similar systems.

Wave function (state function or psi-function): an abstract function in configuration space representing the physical state of the system and such that the square of its absolute value at a point is proportional to the probability of finding the system with the given coordinates.

Wave packet (or probability wave): the wave in coordinate space (analogous with the electromagnetic wave) complementary to the particle representation and with the property that the square of its absolute value at a particular point is proportional to the probability of a particle-like manifestation of the system at that point following a measurement on the system. See *complementarity.*

BIBLIOGRAPHY

Ambacher, Michel. *Méthode de la philosophie de la nature*. Paris: P.U.F., 1961.
Appenzeller, Heinz. "Der Energiebegriff als Grundlage einer Universal-terminologie", *Actes IIe Congrès de Philo.*, (1954), vol. III, pp. 146–151.
Araki, H., and Yanase, M. M. "On the Measurement of Quantum Mechanical Operators", *Phys. Rev.*, cxx (1960), pp. 622–626.
Bavink, Bernard. *Ergebnisse u. Probleme der Naturwissenschaften*. 8th ed. Berlin: 1944.
Bergmann, Gustav. "Physics and Ontology", *Phil. Sci.*, xxviii (1961), pp. 1–14.
Bernays, P. "Ueber den Unterschied zwischen realistischer und konservativer Tendenz in der heutigen theoretischen Physik", *Rev. Mét. Mor.*, lxvii (1962), pp. 142–146.
Blokhintsev, D. *Grundlagen der Quantenmechanik*. Berlin: 1953.
Bohm, D. *Quantum Theory*. New York: Prentice-Hall, 1951.
— "A Suggested Interpretation of the Quantum Theory in terms of 'Hidden Variables'", *Phys. Rev.*, lxxxv (1952), pp. 166–179; 180–193.
— *Causality and Chance in Modern Physics*. Princeton: 1957.
— "A proposed Explanation of the Quantum Theory in terms of hidden variables at a sub-quantum-mechanical level", in *Observation and Interpretation*, ed. by S. Körner, pp. 33–40.
— "Classical and Non-classical Concepts in the Quantum Theory", An answer to Heisenberg's *Physics and Philosophy*, *Brit. Jour. Phil. Sci.*, xii (1961), pp. 265–280.
Bohr, Niels. *Atomic Theory and the Description of Nature*. Cambridge: 1934.
— "Can Quantum Mechanical Description of Physical Reality be considered Complete?" ,*Phys. Rev.*, xlviii (1935), pp. 696–702.
— "Kausalität u. Komplementarität", *Erkenntnis*, vi (1936) pp. 293–303.
— "Newton's Principles and Modern Atomic Mechanics", in *Newton Tercentenary Celebrations*, ed. by the Royal Soc. Cambridge: 1947.
— "On the Notions of Complementarity and Causality", *Dialectica*, ii (1948), pp. 312–317.
— "Discussion with Einstein on Epistemological Problems in Atomic Physics", in *Albert Einstein: Philosopher–Scientist*. Ed. by A. Schilpp. Evanston: 1949.
— "Ueber Erkenntnisfragen der Quantenphysik", in *Max Planck Festschrift*, Berlin: 1959, pp. 169–175.
— *Atomic Physics and Human Knowledge*. New York: John Wiley, 1958.
— "Die Entstehung der Quantenmechanik" in *Werner Heisenberg u. die Physik unserer Zeit*, ed. by F. Bopp. Braunschweig: Vieweg, 1961, pp. ix–xii.
Bopp, Fritz. "The Principle of Statistical Equations of Motion in Quantum Theory", in *Observation and Interpretation*, ed. by S. S. Körner, pp. 189–196.

— (ed.). *Werner Heisenberg und die Physik unserer Zeit*. Braunschweig: Vieweg, 1961.
Born, Max. *The Natural Philosophy of Cause and Chance*. Oxford: Clarendon Press, 1949.
— *Physics in My Generation: A Selection of Papers*. London: Pergamon Press, 1956.
Braithwaite, Richard B. *Scientific Explanation*, Cambridge: 1953.
Bridgman, P. W. *The Logic of Modern Physics*. New York: Macmillan, 1927.
— *The Nature of Physical Theory*. New York: Dover.
— "The Nature of Some of our Physical Concepts, I, II, III", *Brit. Jour. Phil. Sci.*, i (1950), pp. 257–272; ii (1951), pp. 25–44; 142–176.
Büchel, Wolfgang. "Quantenphysik u. naturphilosophischer Substanzbegriff", *Scholastik*, xxxiii (1958), pp. 161–185.
— "Die Diskussion um die Interpretation der Quantenphysik", *Scholastik*, xxix (1954), pp. 235–244.
— "Idealismus oder Realismus? Zur Diskussion um die philosophische Bedeutung der Quantenphysik", *Stimm. Zeit.*, clv (1954), pp. 255–263.
— "Hylomorphismus u. Atomphysik", *Phil. Nat.*, iii (1955), pp. 318–338.
— "Individualität u. Wechselwirkung im Bereich des materiellen Seins", *Scholastik*, xxxi (1956), pp. 1–30.
— "Quantenphysik u. Kritischer Realismus", *Phil. Nat.*, iv (1958).
Bunge, Mario. *Causality: The Place of the Causal Principle in Modern Science*. Oxford: Oxf. U. P., 1959.
— "Strife about Complementarity, I, II", *Brit. Jour. Phil. Sci.*, vi (1955), pp. 1–12; 141–154.
— "Survey of the Interpretations of Quantum Mechanics", *Amer. Jour. Phys.*, xxiv (1956), p. 272.
— *Metascientific Queries*. Springfield: 1959.
Burtt, E. A. *The Metaphysical Foundations of Modern Physical Science*, London: Routledge and Kegan Paul, rev. ed. 1931.
Butterfield, Herbert. *Origins of Modern Science, 1300–1800*, London: Bell, 1957.
Capek, Milic. *The Philosophical Impact of Contemporary Physics*, New York: Van Nostrand, 1961.
Carnap, Rudolf. *Logical Foundations of Probability*, Chicago: Univ. of Chic. Press, 1950.
Cassirer, Ernst. *Determinism and Indeterminism in Modern Physics*, Trans. by T. Benfey. New Haven: Yale U.P., 1956.
— *Substance and Function*. Trans. by W. C. Swabey and M. C. Swabey, New York: Dover, 1953.
Churchman, C. West, and Ratoosh, Philburn (eds.). *Measurement: Definitions and Theories*. New York: John Wiley, 1959.
Collingwood, R. G. *The Idea of Nature*. Oxford: Oxf. U.P., 1945.
Colodny, R. G. and Hempel, C. G. (eds.). *Frontiers of Science and Philosophy*. Pittsburgh: Univ. of Pitts. Press, 1963.
Cornford, Francis M. *Plato's Cosmology: The Timaeus of Plato Translated with a Running Commentary*. New York, Lib. Arts Press. 1957.
Costa de Beauregard, O. *Le second principe de la science de temps*. Paris: Seuil, 1963.
— *La notion de temps*. Paris: Hermann, 1963.
De Broglie, Louis. *Non-Linear Wave Mechanics: A Causal Interpretation*. Amsterdam: Elsevier, 1960.
Destouches, J. L. "Théories prévisionnelles et théories réalistes en microphysique", *Rev. Mét. Mor.*, lvii (1962), pp. 174–205.

Dirac, P. A. M. "Physical Interpretation of Quantum Dynamics", *Prov. Roy. Soc.*, cxiii (1927), pp. 621–641.
— *Principles of Quantum Mechanics*. Oxford: U.P., 1958.
— "The Physicist's Picture of Nature", *Scientific American*, ccviii (1936), pp. 45–53.
Dondeyne, A. *Foi chrétienne et pensée contemporaine*. Louvain: 1961.
Duhem, Pierre. *The Aim and Structure of Physical Theory*. Trans. from the 2nd French edit. Princeton: Princeton U.P., 1954.
Eddington, Sir Arthur. *The Philosophy of Physical Science*. Cambridge: Cambr. U.P., 1949.
Eder, Gernot. "Gibt es 'Bausteine' der Materie? Die Erforschung der Elementarteilchen ihre Eigenschaften u. Metamorphosen", *Wort u. Wahrheit*, xv (1960), pp. 8–9; 524–534.
Einstein, Albert. "Autobiographical Notes", in *Albert Einstein: Philosopher-Scientist*, ed. by A. Schilpp, pp. 2–95.
— "Elementare Ueberlegungen zur Interpretation der Grundlagen der Quantenmechanik", in *Scientific Papers Presented to Max Born*. Edinburgh: 1953, pp. 33–40.
—, Podolsky, B. and Rosen, N. "Can Quantum Mechanical Description of Reality be Considered Complete?", *Phys. Rev.*, xlvii (1935), pp. 777–780.
Feibleman, James K. "On Substance", *Rev. of Metaphys.*, viii (1955), pp. 373–378.
Feigl, Herbert. "Existential Hypotheses", *Phil. Sci.*, xvii (1950), pp. 35–62.
— and Brodbeck, M. (eds.). *Readings in the Philosophy of Science*. New York: Appleton-Century-Crofts, 1053.
—, Scriven, M. and Maxwell, Grover (eds.). *Minnesota Studies in the Philosophy of Science*. Volume I: (eds.) The Foundations of Science and the Concept of Psychology and Psychoanalysis. Minneapolis: Univ. of Minn. Press, 1956.
—, Scriven, M. and Maxwell, Grover (eds.). *Minnesota Studies in the Philosophy of Science*. Volume II: Concepts, Theories and the Mind-Body Problem. Minneapolis: Univ. of Minn. Press, 1958.
— and Maxwell, Grover (eds.). *Minnesota Studies in the Philosophy of Science*. Volume III: Scientific Explanation, Space and Time. Minneapolis, Univ. of Minn. Press, 1962.
— and Maxwell, Grover (eds.). *Current Issues in the Philosophy of Science*. New York: Rinehart and Winston. 1961.
Fényes, I. "Eine wahrscheinlichkeitstheoretische Begründung u. Interpretation der Quantenmechanik", *Zeit. f. Physik*, cxxxii (1952), pp. 81–106.
Février, P. *L'interprétation physique de la mécanique ondulatoire et des théories quantiques*. Paris: Gauthier-Villars, 1956.
Feyerabend, P. K. "Eine Bemerkung zum Neumannischen Beweis", *Zeit. f. Physik*, cxlv (1956), pp. 421–423.
— "Complementarity", *Proc. Arist. Soc.*, Suppl., xxxii (1958) pp. 75–104.
— "On the Quantum Theory of Measurement", in *Observation and Interpretation*, ed. by S. Körner, pp. 121–130.
— "An attempt at a Realistic Interpretation of Experience", *Proc. Arist. Soc.*, lviii (1958), pp. 144–170.
— "Professor Bohm's Philosophy of Nature", *Brit. Jour. Phil. Sci.*, x (1960), pp. 321–338.
— "Problems in Microphysics", in *Frontiers of Science and Philosophy*, ed. by R. G. Colodny and C. G. Hempel, pp. 189–283.
Fierz, M. and Weisskopf, V. F. (eds.). *Theoretical Physics in the Twentieth Century A Memorial Volume to Wolfgang Pauli*. New York: Interscience, 1960.

Fock, V. *Max Planck Festschrift*. Berlin: 1958, p. 177.

Fogarasi, Bela. *Kritik des Physikalischen Idealismus*. Budapest: 1953.

Forest, Aimé. *La structure métaphysique du concret selon St. Thomas d'Aquin*. Paris: Vrin, 1956.

Frank, Philipp. *Philosophy and Science: The Link between Science and Philosophy*. Englewood Cliffs: Prentice-Hall, 1957.

Friedrich, L. W. (ed.). *The Nature of Physical Knowledge*. Milwaukee: Marquette Univ. Press, 1960.

Good, I. J. (ed.) *The Scientist Speculates: An Anthology of Partlybaked Ideas*. London: Heinemann, 1962.

Groenewold, H. J. "Objective and Subjective Aspects of Statistics in Quantum Descriptions", in *Observation and Interpretation*, ed. by S. Körner, pp. 197–208.

Grünbaum, A. "The Role of *A Priori* Elements in Physical Theory", in *The Nature of Physical Knowledge*, ed. by L. W. Friedrichs.

— "Realism and Neo-Kantianism in Professor Margenau's Philosophy of Quantum Mechanics", *Philos. Sci.*, xvii (1950), pp. 26–34.

— "Complementarity in Quantum Physics and its Philosophical Generalisation" *Jour. Philos.*, liv (1957), pp. 713–727.

Guérard de Laurier, L. B. "La substance sensible", I, II, *Angelicum*, xxxix (1962), pp. 40–91; 350–394.

Hanson, Norwood Russell. *Patterns of Discovery*. Cambridge: Cambr. U. P., 1958.

— *The Concept of the Positron*. Cambridge: Cambr. U.P., 1963.

Harré, R. "Philosophy and Quantum Physics", *Philosophy*, xxxv (1960), pp. 341–343.

— *An Introduction to the Logic of the Sciences*. London: Macmillan, 1960.

Heisenberg, W. "Ueber quantentheoretische Umdeutung Kinematischer u. mechanischer Beziehungen", *Zeit. f. Physik*, xxx (1925), pp. 879–893.

— "Ueber quantentheoretischer Kinematik u. Mechanik", *Math. Ann.*, xcv (1926), pp. 683–705.

— "Ueber den anschaulichen Inhalt der quantentheoretischen Kinematik u. Mechanik", *Zeit. f. Physik*, xliii (1927), pp. 172–198.

— *Physical Principles of the Quantum Theory*. Translated by Carl Eckart and F. C. Hoyt. Chicago: Chicago Univ. Press, 1930.

— "Kausalgesetz u. Quantenmechanik", *Erkenntnis*, ii (1931), pp. 172–182. Discussion by Frank, Reichenbach, Herzberg, Meyer, von Neumann, Grelling, Steinhausen and Hamel, pp. 183–188.

— "Wahrscheinlichkeitsaussagen in der Quantentheorie der Wellenfelder", *Actualités scientifiques et industrielles*, No. 734. Paris: Hermann, 1938.

— "Der Begriff 'Abgeschlossene Theorie' in der modernen Naturwissenschaft", *Dialectica*, ii (1948), pp. 331–336.

— "On the Mathematical Framework of the Theory of Elementary Particles", *Commun. Pure Appl. Maths.*, 4 (1951) pp. 15–22.

— *Philosophic Problems of Nuclear Science*, Translated by F. C. Hayes from *Wandlungen in den Grundlagen der Naturwissenschaft* (1949). London: Faber and Faber, 1952. The eight lectures published here are: "Recent Changes in the Foundations of Exact Science" (1934), pp. 11–26; "On the History of the Physical Interpretation of Nature" (1933), pp. 27–40; "Questions of Principle in Modern Physics" (1935), pp. 41–52; "Ideas of the Natural Philosophy of Ancient Times in Modern Physics" (1937), pp. 53–59; "The Teachings of Goethe and Newton on Colour in the Light of Modern Physics" (1941), pp. 60–76; "On the Unity of the Scientific Outlook on Nature" (1941), pp. 77–94; "Fundamental Problems of Present-Day Atomic Physics" (1948), pp. 95–108; "Science as a Means of International Understanding" (1946), pp. 109–120.

— "The Development of the Interpretation of the Quantum Theory", in *Niels Bohr and the Development of Physics*. Edited by W. Pauli. New York: McGraw-Hill, 1955, pp. 12–29.

— *The Physicist's Conception of Nature*. Translated by Arnold J. Pomerans from *Das Naturbild der heutigen Physik* (1955). London: Hutchinson, 1958.

— *Physics and Philosophy: The Revolution in Modern Science*. World Perspectives vol. 19. London: Harper, 1958.

— "Grundlegende Voraussetzungen in der Physik der Elementarteilchen" in *Martin Heidegger zum siebzigsten Geburtstag: Festschrift*. Pfullingen: Neske, 1959, pp. 291–297.

— "Erinnerungen an die Zeit der Entwicklung der Quantenmechanik" in *Theoretical Physics in the Twentieth Century: A Memorial Volume to Wolfgang Pauli*. Edited by M. Fierz and J. F. Weisskopf. New York: Interscience, 1960, pp. 40–47.

— "Die Entwicklung der einheitlichen Feldtheorie der Elementarteilchen", *Naturwissen.*, 1 (1963), pp. 3–7.

—, Born, M. and Jordan, P. "Zur Quantenmechanik II", *Zeit. f. Physik*, xxxv (1926), pp. 557–615.

—, Born, M., Schrödinger, E. and Auger, P. *On Modern Physics*. Translated M. Goodman and J. W. Binns. London: Orion Press, 1961. Heisenberg's contribution is entitled: "Planck's Discovery and the Philosophical Problems of Atomic Physics", pp. 3–20.

Hempel, Carl G. "Deductive-Nomological Vs. Statistical Explanation", in *Minnesota Studies in the Philosophy of Science*, vol. III, ed. by H. Feigl et al. pp. 98–169.

Hilbert, D. *Grundlegende Geometrie*, Leipzig: 1930.

Hoenen, P. *Cosmologia*. 5th ed. Rome: Greg. Univ., 1956.

Husserl, Edmund. *Ideas*. Trans. by W. R. Boyce Gibson. London: Allen and Unwin, 1931.

— *Die Krisis der europäischen Wissenschaften und die transzendentale Phänomenologie*, I and II (1936). Husserliana VI, 1954.

Hutten, Ernest H. *The Language of Modern Physics*. London: Allen and Unwin, 1956.

Jordan, P. *Anachaliche Quantentheorie*. Berlin: 1936.

Kant, Immanuel. *Kritik der reinen Vernunft* (1st ed., 1781; 2nd ed., 1788) *Immanuel Kants Werke*, Bd. III. Berlin: Cassirer, 1912–1922. Trans. into English by N. Kemp-Smith, London, 1929.

— *Die metaphysischen Anfangsgrunde der Naturwissenschaft* (1786). *Immanuel Kants Werke, Bd.* IV. Berlin: Cassirer, 1912–1922. Trans. into French by J. Gibelin. Paris: Vrin, 1952.

— *Prolegomena zu einer jeden künftigen Metaphysik (1783)*. *Immanual Kants Werke, Bd.* IV. Berlin: Cassirer, 1912–1922. Trans. into English by P. E. Lucas Manchester: 1953.

Kapp, Reginald O. "The Observer, the Interpreter and the Object Observed", *Methodos*, vii (1955), pp. 3–10.

Kilbansky, Raymond (ed.). *Philosophy in the Mid-Century: A Survey*. Florence: 1961.

Kneale, William. *Probability and Induction*. Oxford: Oxf. U.P., 1949.

Körner, S. (ed.). *Observation and Interpretation: A Symposium of Philosophers and Physicists*. London: Butterworths Scientific Publ., 1957.

Ladrière, Jean. "Concepts scientifiques et idées philosophiques", in *La relativité de notre connaissance*. Louvain: Instit. Sup. Phil., 1948, pp. 103–156.

— "Philosophy and Science", *Philos. Studies* (Dublin) viii (1958), pp. 3–23.
— "La philosophie des mathématiques et le problème du formalisme", *Rev. Phil. Louvain*, lvii (1959), pp. 600–622.
Landé, A. *Foundation of Quantum Theory: A Study in Continuity and Symmetry.* New Haven, 1955.
— *From Dualism to Unity in Quantum Physics.* Cambridge: Cambr. U.P., 1960.
Laplace: Pierre Simon, Marquis de. *A Philosophical Essay on Probabilities.* Trans. by F. W. Truscott and F. L. Emory. New York: Dover, 1951.
Lenzen, Victor F. "The Interaction between Subject and Object in Observation", *Erkenntnis*, vi (1936–37), pp. 326–335.
London, G. and Bauer, E. *La Théorie de l'observation en mécanique quantique.* Actualités scientifiques et industrielles, No. 775. Paris: Hermann, 1939.
Lonergan, Bernard J. F. "The Concept of 'Verbum' in the Writings of St. Thomas Aquinas", *Theological Studies*, vii (1946), pp. 349–392; viii (1947), pp. 35–79; 404–444; x (1949), pp. 3–40; 359–393.
— "Isomorphism of Thomist and Scientific Thought", *Sapientia Aquinatis* I (1955), pp. 119–127.
— *Insight: A Study of Human Understanding.* London: Longmans, 1957.
Ludwig, G. *Die Grundlagen der Quantenmechanik.* Berlin: Springer, 1954.
— "Gelöste u. ungelöste Probleme des Messprozesses in der Quantenmechanik" in *Werner Heisenberg u. die Physik unserer Zeit*, ed. by F. Bopp, pp. 150–181.
Luyten, Norbert A. "Cosmologie et philosophie scientifique", *Rev. Phil. Louvain*, I (1952), p. 591.
— "Towards a Philosophic Notion of Matter", *Philos. To-day*, vi (1962), ij. 25.
Mach, Ernst. *The Science of Mechanics.* Trans. from the German of the 9th ed. by T. J. McCormack. London: 1942.
MacKinnon, E. "Atomic Physics and Reality", *Mod. Schoolman*, xxxviii (1960), pp. 37–59.
Mansion, Augustin. *Introduction à la physique aristotélicienne.* Louvain-Paris: 1945.
Margenau, Henry. "Reality in Quantum Mechanics", *Philos. Sci.*, xvi (1949), pp. 287–302.
— "Advantages and Disadvantages of Various Interpretations of the Quantum Theory", *Physics To-day*, 7/10 (1954), pp. 6–13.
— *The Nature of Physical Reality.* New York: McGraw-Hill, 1950.
— "Measurements and Quantum States", *Philos. Sci.*, xxx (1963), pp. 1–16; 138–157.
Maxwell, Grover. "The Ontological Status of Theoretical Entities", *Minn. Studies in the Phil. of Science*, III, ed. by H. Feigl, and G. Maxwell, pp. 3–27.
McKnight, J. L. "An Extended Latency Interpretation of Quantum Mechanical Measurement", *Philos. Sci.*, xxv (1958).
McMullin, Ernan. *The Principle of Uncertainty: A Preliminary Critical Study of the Origin, Meanings and Consequences of the Quantum Principle of Uncertainty.* Doctoral Dissertation. Louvain: Institut Supérieur de Philosophie, 1954.
— "Realism in Modern Cosmology", *Proc. Amer. Cath. Phil. Assoc.*, xxix (1955), pp. 137–150.
Montofiore, Alan. "Determinism and Causal Order", *Proc. Arist. Soc.*, lviii (1957–1958), pp. 125–142.
Nagel, Ernest. *The Structure of Science.* London: Routledge and Kegan Paul, 1961.
Newton, T. D. and Wigner, E. P. "Localised States of Elementary Systems", *Rev. Mod. Physics*, xxi (1949), p. 400.

Omel'janowsky, M. E. *Philosophische Probleme der Quantenmechanik.* Trans. from the Russian by Horst Fischer. Berlin: VEB Deut. Verl. Wissen., 1962.
Pap, Arthur. *Introduction to the Philosophy of Science.* London: Eyre and Spottiswoode, 1963.
— *The A Priori in Physical Theory.* New York: 1946.
Pauli, Wolfgang. (ed.). *The Concept of Complementarity. Dialectica,* ii, No. 3/4 (1948).
— "Phänomen u. physikalische Realität", *Dialectica,* xi (1957), pp. 36–48.
— (ed.) *Niels Bohr and the Development of Physics.* London: Pergamon Press, 1955.
Peirce, Charles S. *Essays in the Philos. of Science.* Ed. by Vincent Tomas, New York: Lib. Arts Press, 1957.
Pippard, A. B., Kemmer, N., Hesse, Mary B., Pryce, M., Bohm, D., and Hanson, N. R. *Quanta and Reality: A Symposium.* Nuffield Foundation for the History of Ideas. London: Hutchinson, 1962.
Planck, Max. *Scientific Autobiography and Other Papers.* London: Williams and Norgate, 1950.
Poincaré, Henri. *Science and Hypothesis.* New York: Dover, 1952.
Popper, Karl. "Indeterminism in Quantum Physics and in Classical Physics, I and II", *Brit. Jour. Phil. Sci.,* i (1950), pp. 117–133; 173–195.
— "The Propensity Interpretation of the Calculus of Probability and the Quantum Theory", in *Observation and Interpretation,* ed. by S. Körner, pp. 65–70.
— *The Logic of Scientific Discovery.* London: Hutchinson, 1960.
— *Conjectures and Refutations.* London: Routledge and Kegan Paul, 1963.
Raeymacker, Louis de. *Philosophie de l'être: Essais de synthèse métaphysique.* Louvain: Edit. Instit. Sup. Philos., 1946.
— "The One Voice of Science and the Many Voices of Philosophy", *Philos. To-day,* v(1961), pp. 83–91.
Reese, William (Gen. Ed.). *The Philosophy of Science: The Delaware Seminar,* Volume I. New York: Interscience, 1963.
Reese, William (Gen. Ed.). *The Philosophy of Science: The Delaware Seminar,* Volume II. New York: Interscience, 1963.
Reichenbach, H. *Philosophic Foundations of Quantum Mechanics.* Berkeley: Univ. of Cal. Press, 1944.
— *The Rise of Scientific Philosophy.* Berkeley and Los Angeles: Univ. of Cal. Press, 1951.
— *Modern Philosophy of Science: Selected Essays.* Trans. by Maria Reichenbach. Foreword by R. Carnap. London: 1959.
Renoirte, F. *Cosmology: Elements of a Critique of the Sciences and of Cosmology.* Trans. by J. F. Coffey, New York: Wagner, 1950.
Riet, G. van. *Problèmes d'épistémologie.* Louvain: Bibl. Phil. Louv., 1960.
Rosenfeld, L. "Le conflit épistémologique entre Einstein et Bohr", *Rev. Mét. Mor.,* lxvii (1962), pp. 147–151.
Russell, Bertrand. *Human Knowledge: Its Scope and Limits.* London: 1948.
— *The Analysis of Matter.* London: Kegan Paul, Trench and Trubner, 1927.
Russell, John. *Science and Metaphysics.* London: Sheed and Ward, 1958.
Schilpp, Arthur (ed.). *Albert Einstein: Philosopher-Scientist.* Evanston, III: Libr. of Living Philosophers, 1949.
Schlesinger, G. "The Prejudice of Micro-reduction", *Brit. Jour. Phil. Sci.,* xii (1961–1962), pp. 215–224.
Schlick, M. "Causality in contemporary Physics I and II", *Brit. Jour. Phil. Sci.,* xii (1961), pp. 177–193; 281–298.

Schrödinger, Erwin. *Collected Papers on Wave Mechanics*. London: Blackie, 1928.
— "Die gegenwärtige Lage in der Quantenmechanik", *Naturwissen.*, xxiii (1935) p. 812.
— "Ambiguity of the Wave Function", *Ann. d. Phys.*, xxxii (1938), pp. 49–55.
— "What is an Elementary Particle?", *Endeavour*, ix (1950), pp. 109–116.
— "Are There Quantum Jumps?", *Brit. Jour. Phil. Sci.*, iii (1953), pp. 109–134; 233; 242.
— *Mind and Matter*. Cambridge: Cambr. U.P., 1956.
Scriven, Michael. "The Present Status of Determinism in Physics" (Symposium: Determinism in the Light of Recent Physics), *Jour. Philos.*, liv (1957), pp. 727–741.
Sellars, Wilfred. "The Language of Theories", in *Current Issues in the Philosophy of Science*, ed. by H. Feigl & G. Maxwell, pp. 57–76.
Selvaggi, F. *Cosmologia*, Rome: Greg. Univ., 1959.
Shimony, Abner. "Role of the Observer in Quantum Theory", *Amer. Jour. Physics*, xxxi (1963), pp. 755–773.
Snow, C. P. *The Two Cultures and a Second Look*. Cambridge: Cambr. U.P., 1964.
Soccorsi, Phil. "De physica quantistica et de principiis philosophicis annotationes", *Sapientia Aquinateis*, I, *Communic. IV Congressus Thomistici internat. Romae*, 1955, pp. 160–174.
Stallo, J. B. *Concepts and Theories of Modern Physics*. Oxford: Oxf. U.P., 1960
Steenbergen, F. van. "Sciences positives et existence de Dieu", *Rev. Phil. Louvain*, lvii (1959), pp. 397–414.
Strasser, Stephan. *Phenomenology and the Human Sciences*. Pittsburgh: Duquesne Univ. Press, 1963.
Strauss, M., Gramatzki, H. J. ,Janossy, L., Albrecht, E., Schmellemeier, H., Heuer, H., Fock, V., Fogarasi, B., Stern, V. "Ueber philosophische Fragen der modernen Physik", *Deutsche Zeit f. Philos.* (Berlin), iii (1955), pp. 106–126; 242–246; 358–373; v (1957), pp. 91–113; 113–114; 734–735.
Suppes, Patrick. *Introduction to Logic*. Princeton: Van Nostrand, 1957.
— "Probability Concepts in Quantum Mechanics", *Philos. Sci.*, xxviii (1961), p.p. 378–389.
Tarski, Alfred. *Introduction to Logic and the Methodology of the Deductive Sciences*. London: 1946.
Tollenaere, M. de. "Methodologie d'une cosmologie réflexive", *Arch. de Philos.*, xxv (1962), p. 229.
Tonini, V. "Nouvelles tendences réalistes dans l'interprétation des théories physiques modernes", *Rev. Mét. Mor.*, lxvii (1962), pp. 152–162.
Tonnelat, M. A. "Le part d'idéalisme dans la physique contemporaine", *Rev. Mét. Mor.*, lxvii (1962), pp. 163–173.
Vigier, J. P. "The Concept of Probability in the Frame of the Probabilistic and the Causal Interpretation of Quantum Mechanics", in *Observation and Interpretation*, ed. by S. Körner, pp. 71–92.
Von Mises, R. *Probability, Statistics and Truth*. 2nd Edit. New York: Macmillan, 1957.
Von Neumann, John. *The Mathematical Foundations of Quantum Mechanics*. Trans. from the German by Robert T. Beyer. Princeton: Princeton U.P., 1955.
Vries, Joseph de. "Quid secundum principia S. Thomae dicendum sit de indeterminismo microphysicali?", *Sapientia Aquinatis*, I. Rome, 1955, pp. 193–201.
Waelhens, Alphonse de. *La philosophie et les expériences naturelles*. The Hague: Nijhoff, 1961.
Wartofsky, Marx W. (ed.). *Boston Studies in the Philosophy of Science*. Proc. of the Boston Colloquium, 1961–1962. Dordrecht: Reidel, 1962.

Watanabe, S. "A Model of the Mind-Body Relation in Terms of a Modular Logic", *Synthese*, xiii (1961), pp. 261–302.
Weiss, Paul. "The Elements of the Physical Universe", *Rev. of Metaphys.*, xv (1961), pp. 3–18.
Weisskopf, Victor, "The Quantum Ladder", *Internat. Sci. and Technology*, June, 1963, pp. 62–70.
Weizsäcker, C. F. von. *The History of Nature*. Trans. by F. Wieck. Chicago: Univ. of Chicago Press, 1949.
— *The World of Physics*. Trans. from the German by Marjorie Grene. London: Routledge and Kegan Paul, 1952.
— "Komplementarität und Logik", *Naturwissen.*, xvii (1955), pp. 521–523.
Wetter, Gustave. *Dialectical Materialism*. Trans. from the German by Peter Heath. London: Routledge and Kegan Paul, 1958.
Weyl, H. *The Theory of Groups in Quantum Mechanics*. Trans. from the German by H. P. Robertson. New York: Dover, 1931.
— *The Philosophy of Mathematics and Natural Science*. Princeton: Princeton Univ. Press, 1949.
Whittaker, Sir Edmund. *A History of the Theories of Aether and Electricity: Modern Theories, 1900–1926*. London: Nelson, 1953.
Whyte, L. L. "On the History of Natural Lengths", *Annals of Science*, x (1954), p. 20.
Wigner, Eugene P. "Representations of the Lorentz Group", *Annals of Math.*, xl (1939), p. 149.
— "Two Kinds of Reality", Lecture given at the *Marquette Conference for the Philosophy of Science*, 1961. Princeton: Princeton University, mimeo, 1961.
— "Theorie der quantenmechanischen Messung", *Physiktagung Wien*, 1961. Mosbach, Baden: Physik Verlag, 1962, p. 1.
— "Remarks on the Mind-Body Problem", in *The Scientist Speculates*, ed. by I. J. Good, pp. 284–299.
— "The Problem of Measurement", *Amer. Jour. Physics*, xxxi (1963), p. 6.
— "Symmetry and Conservation Laws", *Proc. Nat. Acad. Sci.* (U.S.A.) 1 (1964), pp. 956–965.
— and Salecker, H. "Quantum Limitations of Measurement of Space-Time Distances", *Phys. Rev.*, cix (1958), p. 571.
Wojciechowski, Jerzy, A. "La relation sujet-objet et la physique quantique", *Rev. Univ. Ottawa*, xxix (1959), pp. 88–89.
Wright, George von. *The Logical Problem of Induction*. 2nd edit. New York: MacMillan, 1957.

INDEX